SOLUBILITY

BY

JOEL H. HILDEBRAND, Ph.D.

Professor of Chemistry in the University of California

American Chemical Society

Monograph Series

BOOK DEPARTMENT

The CHEMICAL CATALOG COMPANY, *Inc.*

19 EAST 24TH STREET, NEW YORK, U. S. A.

1924

COPYRIGHT, 1924, BY

The CHEMICAL CATALOG COMPANY, *Inc.*

Press of
J. J. Little & Ives Company
New York, U. S. A.

GENERAL INTRODUCTION

American Chemical Society Series of
Scientific and Technologic Monographs

By arrangement with the Interallied Conference of Pure and Applied Chemistry, which met in London and Brussels in July, 1919, the American Chemical Society was to undertake the production and publication of Scientific and Technologic Monogrר¹ on chemical subjects. At the same time it was agreed th ᴐ the National Research Council, in coöperation with the American Chemical Society and the American Physical Society, should undertake the production and publication of Critical Tables of Chemical and Physical Constants. The American Chemical Society and the National Research Council mutually agreed to care for these two fields of chemical development. The American Chemical Society named as Trustees, to make the necessary arrangements for the publication of the monographs, Charles L. Parsons, Secretary of the American Chemical Society, Washington, D. C.; John E. Teeple, Treasurer of the American Chemical Society, New York City; and Professor Gellert Alleman of Swarthmore College. The Trustees have arranged for the publication of the American Chemical Society series of (a) Scientific and (b) Technologic Monographs by the Chemical Catalog Company of New York City.

The Council, acting through the Committee on National Policy of the American Chemical Society, appointed the editors, named at the close of this introduction, to have charge of securing authors, and of considering critically the manuscripts prepared. The editors of each series will endeavor to select topics which are of current interest and authors who are recognized as authorities in their respective fields. The list of monographs thus far secured appears in the publisher's own announcement elsewhere in this volume.

3

The development of knowledge in all branches of science, and especially in chemistry, has been so rapid during the last fifty years and the fields covered by this development have been so varied that it is difficult for any individual to keep in touch with the progress in branches of science outside his own specialty. In spite of the facilities for the examination of the literature given by Chemical Abstracts and such compendia as Beilstein's Handbuch der Organischen Chemie, Richter's Lexikon, Ostwald's Lehrbuch der Allgemeinen Chemie, Abegg's and Gmelin-Kraut's Handbuch der Anorganischen Chemie and the English and French Dictionaries of Chemistry, it often takes a great deal of time to coördinate the knowledge available upon a single topic. Consequently when men who have spent years in the study of important subjects are willing to coördinate their knowledge and present it in concise, readable form, they perform a service of the highest value to their fellow chemists.

It was with a clear recognition of the usefulness of reviews of this character that a Committee of the American Chemical Society recommended the publication of the two series of monographs under the auspices of the Society.

Two rather distinct purposes are to be served by these monographs. The first purpose, whose fulfilment will probably render to chemists in general the most important service, is to present the knowledge available upon the chosen topic in a readable form, intelligible to those whose activities may be along a wholly different line. Many chemists fail to realize how closely their investigations may be connected with other work which on the surface appears far afield from their own. These monographs will enable such men to form closer contact with the work of chemists in other lines of research. The second purpose is to promote research in the branch of science covered by the monograph, by furnishing a well digested survey of the progress already made in that field and by pointing out directions in which investigation needs to be extended. To facilitate the attainment of this purpose, it is intended to include extended references to the literature, which will enable anyone interested to follow up the subject in more detail. If the literature is so voluminous that a complete bibliography is impracticable, a critical selection will be made of those papers which are most important.

The publication of these books marks a distinct departure in the policy of the American Chemical Society inasmuch as it is a serious attempt to found an American chemical literature without primary regard to commercial considerations. The success of the venture will depend in large part upon the measure of coöperation which can be secured in the preparation of books dealing adequately with topics of general interest; it is earnestly hoped, therefore, that every member of the various organizations in the chemical and allied industries will recognize the importance of the enterprise and take sufficient interest to justify it.

AMERICAN CHEMICAL SOCIETY

BOARD OF EDITORS

This book is dedicated in grateful acknowledgment to those collaborators with the author in this particular field who have helped to prepare the way for writing it.

BEN LEON GLASCOCK   CLARENCE W. BEEBE
ERMON D. EASTMAN   ELVEN T. ELLEFSON
DONALD B. KEYES   CLARENCE A. JENKS
ALICE D. DUSCHAK   THEOPHIL F. BUEHRER
ANGIER H. FOSTER   THORFIN R. HOGNESS

NELSON W. TAYLOR

PREFACE

This book is the outgrowth of a number of years of rather intensive study of the problem of solubility. The paucity of books upon this subject and its immense importance to all chemists inspire the hope that this work will not be unwelcome.

The author has had a twofold purpose, first to make available for the use of chemists confronted with practical difficulties the means so far available for their solution, and second, to present the subject as an inviting field for research. Like most compromises, this is not altogether satisfactory, for the book will of necessity appear somewhat longwinded to the first group of readers, and too explicit and elementary in parts to the second group. I trust, however, that the arrangement has been such as to make it possible for the reader to select that material which is more relevant to his purpose.

As I write this Preface, just after completing the text, and approach the time when the book shall be launched upon its career, I find the moment one of considerable humility. The subject is a vast and baffling one, and I am conscious of the incompleteness and unsatisfactory character of much of the theory and evidence I have presented. However, this may prove to be not altogether unfortunate, for while it may redound more to the credit of the explorer for him to exhibit a chart showing all parts of the territory completely explored, it is far more stimulating to adventurous people to see a map with regions marked "unexplored." I have tried, accordingly, to label clearly discrepancies and disturbing factors, so far as I have known of their existence, and to suggest relations that seem to promise means of progress which I myself have thus far been unable to utilize. The reader, therefore, who finds the book unsatisfactory so far as adequate knowledge is concerned, will cause me no great unhappiness on that account, provided that there are found some readers who find in the book a stimulus to research in this field, and a few signposts pointing the way. I have no desire to reserve the field, for science is a vast coöperative enterprise, and not a means for personal glorification, and no one individual will solve the problem of solubility.

The existence of discrepancies between theory and fact will probably not be as disturbing to the chemist, who deals with phenomena so complicated that he is reasonably content with a principle that guides him correctly in the majority of instances, as it would be to the physicist whose simpler phenomena he has more successfully reduced to exact formulation. The chemist has been glad to use the Periodic System, even though, for many years, the positions of iodine and tellurium

9

were paradoxical. He will likewise, I am confident, find the theories of solubility here presented exceedingly valuable, despite their inadequacy in many cases.

In presenting a subject upon which so much has been written it has been impossible to give proper reference to the work of all my predecessors. This difficulty has been accentuated by the use of a logical rather than the historical method of presentation. As I have proceeded I have found again and again that ideas which I supposed were original had been uttered before. As age and worldly experience increase, however, one becomes more and more callous to such shocks, just as the cow gradually loses, with increasing maternal experience, the belligerent solicitude displayed for her first offspring. I hope, therefore, that omissions of adequate reference to the works of my predecessors will not unduly disturb anyone who has a passion for priority, for I am prepared, for the sake of peace, to renounce all credit for anything except having synthesized the parts of the comprehensive theory of solubility whose separate consideration heretofore has been responsible for much confusion.

I had intended to add a chapter upon methods for the determination of solubility, but have found that this would have involved great delay in the publication, which would probably be unwise in view of the outlines available elsewhere, particularly in Seidell, "Solubilities of Inorganic and Organic Compounds," Van Nostrand, 1919, and J. V. Eyre, "Solubility," Brit. Assoc. Advancement of Sci. Repts., Pt. I, 1910; Pt. II, 1913.

I am indebted to both of these books for other valuable material, as well as to the well-known book by Rothmund, "Löslichkeit und Löslichkeitsbeeinflüssung," Leipzig, Barth, 1907. Frequent reference has been made to the recent work of my colleagues, Lewis and Randall, "Thermodynamics and the Free Energy of Chemical Substances," McGraw-Hill, 1923. This reference to their book has made it unnecessary for me to repeat here the derivation of numerous thermodynamic formulas which I have wished to use, and to avoid confusion I have retained their notation practically unchanged.

I cannot overstate my indebtedness to colleagues and students in this laboratory whose criticism during a number of years has assisted in the development of the subject. I am grateful also to Professor James Kendall for reading the manuscript and for many helpful criticisms.

JOEL H. HILDEBRAND.

Berkeley, Calif.
August 10, 1923.

CONTENTS

II

SOLUBILITY

Chapter I.

Introductory.

The entire history of chemistry bears witness to the extraordinary importance of solubility. The somewhat mysterious nature of solution and recrystallization invited the speculations of ancient philosophers.[1] The medieval alchemist took an interest in the "Alkahest," or universal solvent, inferior only to his interest in gold and in eternal life.

Although this faith in the existence of a universal solvent survives only in the mind of the freshman who invokes *aqua regia* to dissolve all precipitates, the importance of the subject has not diminished with the development of chemistry, and the chemist encounters some problem in solubility upon every hand. He takes advantage of differences in solubility in the separation and purification of materials, and his methods of analysis are based almost entirely thereon. He selects certain materials for his vessels, both in the laboratory and in the manufacturing plant, largely because they resist the solvent action of the liquids they are to contain; and vice versa, many liquids owe their value in his estimation chiefly to their solvent powers for certain materials. Most of the reactions in which he is interested are brought about in solution and are influenced by the solubilities of the substances involved. Even solid solutions have to be reckoned with in many cases, as in the study of alloys, and in the process of recrystallization.

The subject has, moreover, a much wider scope than is indicated by the ordinary use of the term solubility, for there are many other properties of solutions which depend, either wholly or partially, upon the same factor that helps to determine solubility. The solubility of one substance in another depends fundamentally upon the ease with which the two molecular species are able to mix, and if the two species display a certain hostility towards mixing, not only will saturation be attained at smaller concentration, but in the unsaturated solution the tendency to mutual segregation will give rise to a partial separation or adsorption of one species at the surface, with a consequent lowering of surface tension. It is likely also to give rise to an expansion and

[1] The history of theories of solution is treated in a very entertaining fashion in a book by P. Walden, "Die Lösungstheorien in Ihrer Geschichtlichen Aufeinanderfolgerung," Ahren's "Sammlung Chemisch Technischer Vorträge," Enke, Stuttgart, 1910.

15

adsorption of heat upon mixing, phenomena not ordinarily connected with solubility.

Again, while we are not accustomed to think of the various methods for determining molecular weights of dissolved substances as having anything to do with solubility, yet the lowering of the freezing point of a liquid on the addition of a solute is dependent upon the ease with which the two species of molecules mix with each other, and may be different for two solutes in the same solvent, even though the solutes have the same molecular weight. To put the matter in another way, we may say that the composition of a solution having a certain freezing point expresses the solubility of the solid form of the "solvent" at the temperature in question, and it is not difficult to see that this solubility may be influenced by some of the same factors that influence the solubility of the "solute." A knowledge of the laws of solubility is therefore essential to the correct interpretation of the data regarding molecular weights in solution.

In general, then, we may note that the same forces which determine the composition of a solution saturated with respect to one of its components, whether the latter is a solid, a liquid, or a gas at some definite pressure, operate not only when the solution is saturated but when it is more dilute with respect to this component, and will influence all the properties connected with the escaping tendency of the molecules. This escaping tendency may be manifested as vapor pressure, in which case we may have to do with vapor pressure-composition data, boiling points and fractional distillation, solubilities of gases, etc. If the escaping tendency is measured by escape into a second solvent immiscible with the first, we have to do with partition coefficients. If the molecules escape from the solution to form a pure solid, we have to do with solubilities of solids, freezing point-composition diagrams, molecular weights by the freezing point method, and fractional crystallization. Where one component escapes through a semipermeable membrane into its own pure liquid we speak of osmotic pressure. Where the molecular species in question can escape by taking advantage of the gain or loss of an electron we have to do with electrode potentials. Where the escape is within the solution itself to form some new molecular species, we have a chemical reaction, whose speed and equilibrium concentrations will be related to the solubilities of the substances involved.

Our fundamental problem, therefore, is to determine so far as possible how the escaping tendencies of the various components of a solution may be expected to vary, first, with the composition of the solution, and second, with the nature of the components. It is evident that this is a problem of great importance, both from the theoretical and the practical standpoints, and that much of modern physical chemistry is concerned with it.

It is equally evident, however, from the slow progress that has been made in its solution, that the problem is beset with many difficulties. The chemist is usually acquainted with but few rules for his guidance beyond the simple maxim that "like dissolves like," which, though we make it more impressive by quoting it in Latin, is of but limited usefulness because it leaves open the question as to what are the criteria for likeness. It has not been easy to connect the solubility of zinc sulfate and the insolubility of barium sulfate in water with any of the other properties of these substances, or to predict whether benzene or carbon tetrachloride is a better solvent for phosphorus, or to explain why phenanthrene is more soluble than anthracene in benzene. The organic chemist makes continual use of the process of recrystallization for the purification of his preparations, but what criterion has he for the choice of a solvent beyond the presence of a bottle of alcohol or ether upon the neighboring shelf?

The problem of solubility is thus highly practical and, at the same time very fascinating from a theoretical standpoint. The author has been sufficiently ambitious to hope that this book might prove of value to the chemist who is confronted with some practical difficulty and also serve as a stimulus to further needed investigations. Accordingly, deductions of value have been emphasized by italic type for the benefit of those who may not care to devote the study necessary to understand, in all cases, the processes whereby they have been obtained. For the second group there has been included considerable information that has come to the author's attention and which he hopes may prove suggestive for advances in the theory of solubility that he himself has thus far been unable to make.

The book may be considered as divided into two main parts, Chapters I to X being devoted chiefly to the presentation of the various aspects of a comprehensive theory of solubility; Chapters XI to XVIII, chiefly to the application of the theories to existing data, the study of which should develop some skill on the part of the reader in the independent use of the theory.

Chapter II.

Methods of Expressing Solubility.

The Solvent and the Solute.

It is customary to regard one of the components of a binary solution as the solvent, or dispersing medium, the other as the solute, or substance which goes into solution. It is well to remember, however, that this distinction is somewhat arbitrary. For example, we ordinarily consider ammonia as a solution of ammonia gas in water, ammonia being the solute and water the solvent. It would be quite as appropriate, however, to consider it as a solution of water vapor in liquid ammonia, and to designate liquid ammonia as the solvent and water as the solute. It is, of course, most convenient to make the solution by passing ammonia gas into water, so that we are most interested in the relation between the amount of ammonia in the solution and the partial pressure of ammonia gas in equilibrium with it. We thus prefer to regard water as the solvent medium, and the ammonia gas as the solute, and speak of the amount of ammonia in a given amount of solution as the solubility of the ammonia in water at the particular temperature and pressure in question.

Again, if we dissolve silver nitrate in water we speak of the former as the solute and latter as the solvent, and if the solution is in equilibrium with the solid salt its composition represents the solubility of silver nitrate in water at the corresponding temperature. If, however, the solution is in equilibrium with ice there is no reason why we should not regard it as saturated with ice, and its composition as representing the solubility of ice in the liquid, in which case the ice might be called the solute.

When we consider a pair of partly miscible liquids, like ether and water, this interchangeability is even more striking. There is, however, no great danger of ambiguity in the designation of solvent and solute, for common usage furnishes two guides. First, we are accustomed to designate the substance present in small amount as the solute. In the ether-water system, we do not hesitate to say that in the layer richer in water the ether is dissolved in the water, making the ether the solute, while in the layer richer in ether the water is dissolved in the ether, and is the solute. Second, where the solution is saturated with one component, and we can refer to the composition of the solution as expressing the solubility of that component, we consider it to be the solute, although, as would be the case with a saturated solution of naphthalene in benzene at 70°, it far exceeds the solvent in amount. Mortimer [1] defines the solute as that component which first crystallizes out on cooling the system. But we should not allow these conventions to obscure the fact that the rôles of solvent and solute are interchangeable, and that no absolute significance should be attached to them.

DESIGNATION OF COMPONENTS.

The components of a solution are the molecular species from which it may be regarded as being made up, and which must be specified in stating its composition. It is usually quite obvious which are the components, but in some cases, as in dealing with solutions of hydrated salts, the composition of the solution may be expressed in terms of different sets of components. Thus the composition of a solution made by dissolving $Na_2SO_4.10H_2O$ in water might be expressed in terms of the amount either of the hydrate or of the anhydrous salt in a given amount of water. Until some theoretical advantage is discovered for one of these ways, either may be used, for either can be converted into the other by a simple calculation. It should be remembered, however, that a solution is not saturated with respect to a component, but with respect to a phase. A solution containing certain relative amounts of the components Na_2SO_4 and H_2O may be saturated with respect to the phase $Na_2SO_4.10H_2O$ but unsaturated with respect to $Na_2SO_4.7H_2O$, or to Na_2SO_4 or to ice. Or again, water may be saturated with respect to ether vapor at some low pressure while still unsaturated with respect to liquid hydrous ether. In stating solubilities, therefore, we should be careful to state the phase referred to.

METHODS OF EXPRESSING SOLUBILITIES.

Solubilities may be expressed in any of the terms which serve to indicate the relative amounts of the components. The weights or the number of mols of the components serve for solutions of all types. Where a component can be measured in the form of a liquid or a gas its volume can serve as a measure of the amount taken. In the case of a gas the pressure also must be specified, and if both components are volatile one must know whether the pressure stated is partial or total pressure.

We may express the composition of a solution as the amount of one component in a certain amount of the other, or as the amount of one component in a certain amount of solution. For example, a solution of 25 g. of iodine in 100 g. of benzene contains 20 g. of iodine in 100 g. of solution. A solution of 12 mols of naphthalene in 108 mols of hexane contains 10 mols of naphthalene in 100 mols of solution. The naphthalene is 0.1 of the total number of mols in the

---

[1] Mortimer, *J. Am. Chem. Soc.*, **44**, 1416 (1922).

solution, and we say that its *mol fraction* is 0.1. In the following pages we shall denote weight by w, number of mols by n, and mol-fraction by N. We shall use subscripts, 1, 2, 3, etc., to distinguish the components of a solution. Where it is desirable to distinguish between solvent and solute we shall use 1 for former and 2 for the latter. The weight ratio of component 1 is the w_1/w_2; its weight percent 100 $w_1/(w_1 + w_2)$; its mol ratio,

$$r_1 = n_1/n_2; \tag{1}$$

its mol fraction,

$$N_1 = n_1/(n_1 + n_2); \tag{2}$$

and its mol percent, $100n_1/(n_1 + n_2)$. We may note the useful relation

$$N_1 + N_2 = 1, \tag{3}$$

since,

$$\frac{n_1}{n_1 + n_2} + \frac{n_2}{n_1 + n_2} = 1.$$

Where more than 2 components are present the weight fraction and mol fraction are more satisfactory for expressing composition, and we have in general the expressions for the weight fractions of the various components,

$$w_1/(w_1 + w_2 + w_3 + \ldots\,); \quad w_2/(w_1 + w_2 + w_3 + \ldots\,), \quad \text{etc.,}$$

and for the mol fractions,

$$N_1 = \frac{n_1}{n_1 + n_2 + n_3 + \ldots}; \quad N_2 = \frac{n_2}{n_1 + n_2 + n_3 + \ldots} \text{ etc., } \tag{4}$$

and likewise

$$N_1 + N_2 + N_3 + \ldots = 1. \tag{5}$$

The above units may be mixed, as when the composition of a solution is stated in terms of number of mols of solute per 100 g. of solvent. This practice is common with aqueous solutions, the molal solution being often defined as the number of mols of solute per 1000 g. of water.

The practice is also common of stating the composition of a solution in terms of weight or number of mols of solute per 1000 cc. of solvent or of solution. The disadvantage of this method is that the volume changes with the temperature, so that if the solution is, say, 0.1 molal at one temperature, it is not 0.1 molal at another temperature, and to change from one temperature to another requires a knowledge of the density of the pure solvent or of the solution, the latter being seldom known. Also, the expression of the amounts of the different components by different units tends to obscure the interchangeability of the rôles of solvent and solute pointed out at the beginning of this chapter.

The solubilities of a gas which obeys Henry's law (that the amount of gas which dissolves in a given amount of liquid is proportional to the partial pressure of the gas) may be stated without reference to the partial pressure of the gas by defining it as the ratio of the volume of the gas to the volume of the liquid in which it dissolves because, although the weight of gas dissolving is proportional to its partial pressure, its volume is *inversely* proportional to its partial pressure, so that the *volume* dissolving in a given amount of liquid is nearly independent of the pressure. Another definition of gas solubility also in use is identical with the above except that the volume of the gas is given at standard conditions.

To illustrate the conversion of one expression for solubility into the others, let us start with the solubility of iodine in carbon bisulfide at 25° as found by experiment, 20.37 g. of iodine per 100 g. of carbon bisulfide. This corresponds to 20.37 g. of iodine in 120.37 g. of *solution*, or 16.92 g. per 100 g. of solution. Taking the density of carbon bisulfide at 25° as 1.253, we calculate that 100 g. of it has a volume of 79.7 cc.; so that the above solution contains 20.37 g. iodine in 79.7 cc. of *solvent*, or 25.5 g. per 100 cc. of solvent. If we knew the density of the solution we might calculate similarly the weight of iodine in 100 cc. of *solution*. Again, taking the molecular weight of iodine as 253.8 and that of carbon bisulfide as 76.1, the solution contains $\frac{20.37}{253.8}$ mol of iodine in $\frac{100}{76.1}$ mol of carbon bisulfide, corresponding to 0.0611 mol of iodine per mol of carbon bisulfide, or 0.0576 mol per mol of mixture, which is its mol fraction. Finally, the mol fraction of *carbon bisulfide* in the solution is 1 — 0.0576 or 0.9424. Other expressions, such as mols of iodine in 100 cc. of solution can similarly be calculated when the necessary data are at hand.

In the development of a theory of solubility it is exceedingly important to decide which definition of solubility to adopt. The relative solubilities of a series of solutes in the same solvent are not the same for the different ways of expressing solubility. Thus benzene at 25° dissolves the following amounts of p-dibromobenzene and naphthalene.

	Wt. fraction	Mol fraction
p-$C_6H_4Br_2$	0.455	0.217
$C_{10}H_8$	0.401	0.290

Expressed in weight-fraction the p-dibromobenzene is more soluble, while in mol fraction the naphthalene is more soluble. It is evident from the foregoing paragraphs that for theoretical purposes, the solubility should be expressed in a way that makes no fundamental distinction between the component we may be pleased to call the solute and the one we call the solvent, i.e., the amounts of the components should be expressed in the same units. Second, the volumes of the components, whether as liquids or gases, though often convenient measures, are dependent on temperature and pressure and are not of any fundamental significance. Third, we should recall that the gram-molecule or mol always has greater significance to the chemist than any other measure of the amount of substance. For these reasons, and for others that will be apparent in the following chapter, the mol fraction will be used throughout the book as the proper basis for developing the theory of solubility. It is simple and easily understood, is not a function of pressure or temperature, and all other means of expressing the composition of solutions can readily be calculated from it. The only ambiguity is that which enters in the case of substances whose molecular weights are doubtful, as with liquid water, or ionized salts. In such cases the molecular weight used will have to be stated.

Chapter III.

The Ideal Solution—Raoult's Law.

Significance of the Ideal Solution.

In Chapter I it was pointed out that the problem of solubility could be divided into two parts. In the first place we may consider how the escaping tendency of any component of a solution varies with the composition of the solution, and in the second place, how this escaping tendency depends upon the specific characters of the components. The value of thus dividing the problem may perhaps be made clearer by pointing out the corresponding division which we make in the study of gas mixtures, where we are accustomed to consider, first, the ideal gas, where the pressure of mixtures is strictly additive, and where the effect of temperature and pressure is given by the equation $PV = nRT$; second, deviations from this behavior on the part of actual gases due to intermolecular attractive forces and molecular volumes, such as are considered in the familiar equation of van der Waals; and third, the deviations from the behavior of ideal gases which may be ascribed to the formation of new molecular species, and where, accordingly, we speak of chemical reactions.

Since the kinetic theory not only gives us the laws of the ideal gas but shows that deviations of the van der Waals type may be minimized by having the gas at low pressures and high temperatures, we feel confident that when deviations from these laws are encountered under such conditions we are justified in ascribing them to chemical changes. For example, when a given amount of iodine vapor is heated at constant pressure its volume increases at a rate closely corresponding with the law of Gay-Lussac until about 700°, when it begins to expand more rapidly, and does not again attain the normal rate until about 1700°. We explain this behavior by assuming dissociation of the iodine from diatomic to monatomic molecules. Similarly when we find that NO_2 fails to obey the gas laws we use the deviation to calculate the equilibrium for the chemical reaction, $2N_2O = N_2O_4$.

In the study of liquid solutions, likewise, it is advantageous to begin by a consideration of the ideal solution before attempting to discuss either of the sources of deviation that have been mentioned in connection with deviations from the behavior of ideal gases.

DEFINITIONS OF THE IDEAL SOLUTION.

Three expressions have been used for defining the relation between escaping tendency and composition in an ideal solution. The most familiar of these and the most important historically is the law of van't Hoff for osmotic pressure, according to which the osmotic pressure of a solution measured against the pure solvent is numerically equal to the pressure which the solute would exert as an ideal gas under the same conditions. The relation between the osmotic pressure, volume of solution, number of mols of solute and the absolute temperature is thus given as $\Pi V = n_2 RT$, where the constant R has the same value as in the equation for the ideal gas.

At nearly the same time that van't Hoff discovered this relation Raoult announced his law for the lowering of the vapor pressure, according to which the ratio of the lowering of the vapor pressure due to the addition of a solute to the vapor pressure of the pure solvent is equal to the ratio of the number of mols of solute to the total number of mols. If $p_1°$ denotes the vapor pressure of the substance X_1 in the pure state, and p_1 its (partial) vapor pressure from a solution of n_1 mols of X_1 with n_2 mols of X_2, then the above relation may be expressed by the equation

$$\frac{p_1° - p_1}{p_1°} = \frac{n_2}{n_1 + n_2}; \qquad (1)$$

or in slightly simpler form as

$$p_1 = p_1° \frac{n_1}{n_1 + n_2} = p_1° N_1, \qquad (2)$$

where N_1 is the mol fraction of X_1. The behavior of the other component is, of course, given by the corresponding equation

$$p_2 = p_2° N_2. \qquad (3)$$

The third relation used to define the ideal solution is Henry's law for the solubility of gases in liquids. As originally announced it stated that the amount of gas dissolving in a given volume of the solvent is proportional to the partial pressure of that gas above the solution. (The conception of partial pressure is due to Dalton.) If instead of expressing the solubility of the gas in terms of volume concentration we express it in terms of mol fraction, we get an expression similar to that for Raoult's law,

$$p_2 = k N_2, \qquad (4)$$

the difference being only in the proportionality constant, k. In fact, Raoult's law may be regarded as a special case of Henry's law.

COMPARISON OF LAWS OF VAN'T HOFF AND RAOULT.

Although at first glance these relations may seem to deal with different phenomena, and therefore not to be regarded as substitutes for each other, this does not prove to be the case, for whenever a relation such as the expressions for lowering of freezing point, rise of boiling point, e.m.f. of concentration cells, etc., can be derived from van't Hoff's law, a corresponding one can be derived from Raoult's law. Henry's law cannot directly serve quite so fully because the constant k is an empirical constant. Van't Hoff, however, based his theoretical proof of his osmotic pressure law upon the assumed validity of Henry's law, so that the former rests upon a no more secure theoretical foundation than the latter.

The almost universal acceptance of the van't Hoff law is undoubtedly due, first, to the fact that van't Hoff showed its significance by deriving from it a number of important relationships, founding for the first time a comprehensive theory of dilute solutions, and second, to the identity in form of this law with the ideal gas law, so that the type of calculation with which chemists were familiar in dealing with gases simply had to be repeated for dissolved substances. For example, the frequently used expression for the work done in the isothermal expansion of a gas

$$\int_V^{V'} P dV = nRT \ln \frac{V'}{V},$$

becomes, when a solution is diluted by the addition of solvent through an osmotic piston,

$$\int_V^{V'} \Pi dV = nRT \ln \frac{V'}{V}.$$

This formal identity with a universally accepted gas law made it easy for chemists to feel that the van't Hoff law was a sort of theoretical necessity, and even at the present time most writers of texts on physical chemistry and even many teachers of general chemistry seem to consider an understanding of osmotic pressure as prerequisite to the further study of physical chemistry.

While it is true that the laws of van't Hoff and Raoult become identical at infinite dilution, in concentrated solutions they yield very different results, and it is necessary for us to choose between them for the further pursuit of our topic. There are several reasons for preferring Raoult's law for our definition of the ideal solution. In the first place it rests upon a more satisfactory theoretical basis. If we consider a binary liquid mixture whose molecules are sufficiently alike in the attractive forces they exert so that a given molecule is under the same attractive and repulsive forces in the mixture as in its own pure liquid, then it is obvious that the tendency of that molecule to escape from the liquid phase (which is measured by its partial vapor pressure), is independent of the composition of the mixture. However, the partial vapor pressure of that component, is determined not only by the escaping tendency of a single molecule but also by the number of molecules, so that the partial vapor pressure of X_1 is to its saturation pressure as the number of molecules of X_1 is to the total number of molecules, or $p_1/p_1^\circ = n_1/(n_1 + n_2) = \text{N}_1$.

We may state this in another way by considering a portion of X_1 in equilibrium with its vapor, and imagining a certain fraction of the molecules of X_1 changed to another species, X_2, which is sufficiently like X_1 to avoid any change in the escaping tendency of the molecules. Obviously the reduction in the proportion of molecules of X_1 in the liquid from I to N_1 will be accompanied by an equal reduction in the vapor phase, so that the partial vapor pressure of X_1 is reduced to the same fraction of its former value.

If we can discover a satisfactory measure of the likeness of the two species, it is evident, first, that we will be able to predict what substances will obey this relation, and second, that deviations from Raoult's law will be related to differences in these intermolecular forces between the two liquids. A comprehensive theory of solutions, therefore, may be based upon Raoult's law and deviations therefrom.

We may note here that the same logic can be applied to systems of more than two components. If n_3 mols of a third substance, X_3, are present, the above reasoning would give for the partial vapor pressure of the respective components,

$$p_1 = p_1^\circ \text{N}_1 = p_1^\circ n_1/(n_1 + n_2 + n_3),$$
$$p_2 = p_2^\circ \text{N}_2 = p_2^\circ n_2/(n_1 + n_2 + n_3),$$
$$p_3 = p_3^\circ \text{N}_3 = p_3^\circ n_3/(n_1 + n_2 + n_3).$$

The law of van't Hoff cannot be directly derived from such simple kinetic considerations. The method used to derive the gas laws for an ideal gas upon the basis of the kinetic theory is not strictly valid when applied to osmotic pressure.

A second advantage of Raoult's law is its agreement with the experimental data for a large number of solutions over the entire range of concentration, while the equation of van't Hoff not only lacks experimental confirmation at higher concentrations but actually leads to absurd figures, for as the proportion of solvent in the solution approaches zero the osmotic pressure actually approaches infinity, while according to the equation of van't Hoff it should never exceed a few hundred atmospheres.[1]

Various attempts have been made to modify the equation of van't Hoff, but they may for the most part be regarded as purely empirical attempts to make the equation agree with a given set of data, and so are of little significance in connection with our present problem.

It is evident that where deviations from ideal behavior on the part of individual solutions are used to calculate chemical changes such as association, dissociation and solvation, very different figures will be obtained according as van't Hoff's law or Raoult's law is used to define

[1] A full discussion of the relation between the laws of van't Hoff and of Raoult together and a modification of the latter proposed by Morse and Frazier has been published by G. N. Lewis, *J. Am. Chem. Soc.*, 30, 668 (1908).

the ideal solution, and we shall see later that even deviations from Raoult's law do not in many cases justify the calculation of the extent of such chemical changes. The absurdity of such calculations is illustrated by one published instance in which the calculated water of hydration of a dissolved substance far exceeded in amount all of the water present!

In a later chapter we shall see that even Raoult's law is not altogether satisfactory for defining the ideal solution, and will discuss more fully the requirements of a satisfactory law for this purpose, but since we are able to predict with considerable certainty when Raoult's law may be expected to hold, it will be well first to consider what solubility relations follow from it.

STATEMENT OF RAOULT'S LAW WHEN THE VAPOR CANNOT BE REGARDED AS A PERFECT GAS. THE FUGACITY.

In pointing out the kinetic basis of Raoult's law in the preceding paragraphs, it was assumed that the tendency of a molecule to escape from a liquid is proportional to the pressure it exerts in the vapor phase. This is true only in so far as the vapor behaves as a perfect gas, which is never strictly the case. It is therefore, desirable to retain the conception of the escaping tendency for the accurate statement of the law, and to inquire how far the vapor pressure deviates from it, avoiding the necessity of assuming, as so many writers have been forced to do in dealing with vapors, that they behave as perfect gases.

G. N. Lewis [2] has treated this subject exhaustively, introducing a term "fugacity," denoted by f, as a measure of escaping tendency. "The fugacity bears to the vapor pressure a relation analogous to the relation between the perfect gas thermometer and a thermometer of some actual gas. The fugacity will be equal to the vapor pressure when the vapor is a perfect gas, and in general may be regarded as an 'ideal' or 'corrected' vapor pressure."

The relation between fugacity and pressure is defined by the equation:

$$\left(\frac{\partial \ln f}{\partial P}\right) = \frac{v}{RT},\qquad(5)$$

and by the relation that the two approach equality as the pressure approaches zero. Various methods for calculating the fugacity of a gas are given in the work by Lewis and Randall, but it will be sufficient for our purpose to give a few of them very briefly.

Deviations from the ideal gas law may be expressed by α in the equation:

$$v = \frac{RT}{P} - \alpha.\qquad(6)$$

[2] G. N. Lewis, *Proc. Am. Acad.*, **37**, 49 (1901); *Z. physik. Chem.*, **38**, 205 (1901); Lewis and Randall, "Thermodynamics; and the Free Energy of Chemical Substances." McGraw-Hill Book Co., New York, 1923.

The fugacity is then given by

$$RT \ln f = RT \ln P - \int_0^P \alpha dP. \tag{7}$$

The integral may be evaluated by plotting α against P and getting the area between the limits.

It has been found that α approaches a constant value at lower pressures, giving

$$\ln \frac{f}{P} = - \frac{\alpha P}{RT}, \tag{8}$$

and since $10^{-x} = 1 - x$ when x is small,

$$\frac{f}{P} = 1 - \frac{\alpha P}{RT} = \frac{Pv}{RT}; \tag{9}$$

or, if P_i denotes the pressure of the ideal gas, which is RT/v,

$$\frac{f}{P} = \frac{P}{P_i}. \tag{10}$$

To illustrate the application of the last formula, let us consider fluorobenzene, which, according to Young,[3] has a saturation pressure of 1.974 atmospheres at $T = 382.0°K$. The molal volume of the vapor under these conditions is 15,000 cc. The ideal gas pressure of this volume of vapor would be $RT/v = 82.07 \times 382 \div 15,000$ or 2.085 atmospheres. Substituting this for P_i in Equation 10 gives

$$\frac{f}{P} = \frac{P}{P_i} = \frac{1.974}{2.085} = 0.947,$$

and $f = 1.87$ atmospheres.

Again, taking the weight of 1 liter of chlorine as 3.220 g., at 0° and 1 atmosphere, the molal volume becomes 22,030 cc. The value of RT/P being 22,410 cc., α in Equation 6 becomes 380 cc. To find the fugacity of the saturated vapor at 0°, where the saturation pressure is 3.66 atmospheres we can use Equation 9 getting

$$\frac{f}{3.66} = 1 - \frac{380}{82 \times 273} \times 3.66 = 0.94,$$

and $f = 3.44$ atmospheres.

These examples serve to illustrate the magnitude of the error made in similar cases by the common assumption that a saturated vapor obeys the gas laws.

Since we would expect escaping tendencies to be proportional to mol fractions with solutions of similar molecular species even though the vapors deviate considerably from the ideal gas laws, it is preferable to state Raoult's law in terms of fugacity when accuracy is sought.

[3] Young, *Phil. Mag.*, **33**, 153 (1892).

Letting $f_1°$, $f_2°$, etc., denote the fugacities of the species X_1, X_2, etc., in the pure liquid form, and f_1, f_2, etc., their respective fugacities from a solution whose composition is expressed as before by the mol fractions N_1, N_2, etc., we have as our formal expression,

$$f_1 = f_1° N_1; \quad f_2 = f_2° N_2, \text{ etc.} \tag{11}$$

OTHER EXPRESSIONS FOR RAOULT'S LAW.

It is well to recognize Raoult's law in various other expressions which may easily be derived from the one previously used. Thus we may write

$$\ln f_1 = \ln f_1° + \ln N_1, \tag{12}$$

and the differentials,

$$\frac{df_1}{dN_1} = f_1° \ (13); \ \frac{d^2 f_1}{dN_1^2} = 0 \ (14); \ \frac{df_1}{dN_1} = \frac{f_1}{N_1} \ (15); \ \frac{d\ln f_1}{d\ln N_1} = 1. \ (16)$$

The last three follow also from Henry's law, and are therefore more general than 11, 12 and 13.

The decrease in free energy which takes place when a mol of one component is transferred from the pure liquid state to an infinite amount of solution is equal to the work done in an ideal distillation process, so that we may write

$$\Delta F_1 \text{ (liquid to solution)} = \overline{F}_1 - F_1° = RT \ln \frac{f_1}{f_1°}, \tag{17}$$

and since $f_1/f_1° = N_1$, for an ideal solution,

$$\Delta F_{1,i} \text{ (liquid to solution)} = RT \ln N_1. \tag{18}$$

Equations 12 to 18 are, of course, approximately true if partial vapor pressures are used in place of fugacities.

Often we are ignorant of the separate values of f and $f°$ but can determine their ratio, $f/f°$. It is therefore useful to define this ratio as the *"activity"*[4] of the component in question giving

$$a_1 = f_1/f_1°, \ a_2 = f_2/f_2°, \ a_3 = f_3/f_3°, \text{ etc.} \tag{19}$$

Raoult's law then becomes

$$a_1 = N_1, \ a_2 = N_2, \ a_3 = N_3, \text{ etc.} \tag{20}$$

[4] Lewis and Randall, "Thermodynamics," Chap. XXII.

Chapter IV.

Solubility Relations Based Upon Raoult's Law.

Partial Vapor Pressures.

Raoult's law is a direct expression of the solubility of a vapor in a solution. Where it holds, and where the saturation pressure of the pure liquid component is known, the mol fraction in the solution is given by the ratio of the partial vapor pressure above the solution to the saturation pressure of the pure vapor, i.e., $N = p/p°$. Let us consider, for example, a solution of carbon tetrachloride in stannic chloride, where Raoult's law is doubtless followed rather closely. The vapor pressures of pure carbon tetrachloride and stannic chloride at 40° are 211 mm. and 51 mm. respectively. If the partial vapor pressure of carbon tetrachloride vapor in equilibrium with the solution of the two liquids is kept at, say, 45 mm., which is 45/211 of the saturation pressure, the mol fraction of the carbon tetrachloride in the solution will have the same value, 0.213, and the mol fraction of stannic chloride will be $1 - 0.213$ or 0.787. We may further calculate the partial vapor pressure of the latter, from the equation $p/51 = 0.787$, giving p = 40 mm.

Total Vapor Pressure.

We may proceed further to calculate the total vapor pressure and the composition of the vapor as compared with that of the solution. The total vapor pressure is, from the above figures, 45 mm. + 40 mm, or 85 mm. The mol fractions of the components in the vapor state in equilibrium with solution of the above composition are, by Dalton's law of partial pressures, 45/85 = 0.53 and 40/85 = 0.47 (or $1 - 0.53$) respectively. If the solution were boiled under these conditions the carbon tetrachloride would be enriched in the first portions of distillate from mol fraction 0.213 to mol fraction 0.53.

The relation between the partial vapor pressures of the components, the total vapor pressures and the mol fractions in the liquid phase is represented graphically in Fig. 1, where the algebraic relations used above, i.e.,

$$p_1 = p_1°N_1, \quad p_2 = p_2°N_2,$$

and

$$p_1 + p_2 = p_1°N_1 + p_2°N_2 = N_1(p_1° - p_2°) + p_2°, \tag{1}$$

have an obvious geometric significance.

30

BOILING POINT-COMPOSITION CURVE.

When the vapor pressures of the pure liquids are known throughout a range of temperature it is possible to calculate the boiling point-composition curve, so useful in connection with the problem of frac-

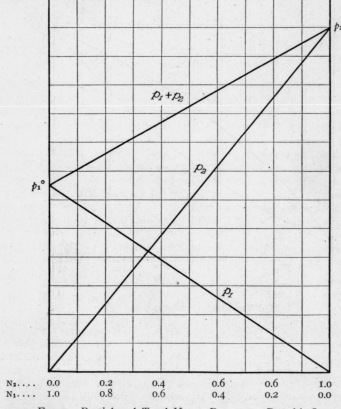

| N₂.... | 0.0 | 0.2 | 0.4 | 0.6 | 0.6 | 1.0 |
| N₁.... | 1.0 | 0.8 | 0.6 | 0.4 | 0.2 | 0.0 |

FIG. 1.—Partial and Total Vapor Pressures—Raoult's Law.

tional distillation. Suppose we have given the following vapor pressures for CCl₄ and SnCl₄:

	t	77°	80°	90°	100°	110°	114°
CCl₄	p₁	760	836	1112	1450	1880	...
SnCl₄	p₂	...	258	362	499	673	760
N₁ {Liquid	..	1.000	0.868	0.531	0.274	0.072	0.000
{Vapor	..	1.000	0.955	0.777	0.523	0.178	0.000

At the boiling point $p_1 + p_2 = 760$ mm., and by Equation 1 above

$$N_1 = (760 - p_2°)/(p_1° - p_2°). \qquad (2)$$

From the known values of p_1° and p_2° at any temperature we can calculate N_1 (and N_2) giving the values in the third row of the table. These can be plotted against the corresponding temperatures to get the boiling point-composition curve shown in Fig. 2. The composition of the vapor, and hence the distillate from liquid of the composition

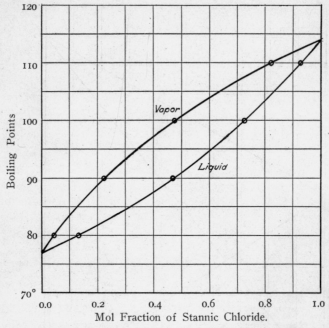

FIG. 2.—Boiling Point—Composition Curves for Stannic Chloride—Carbon Tetrachloride Mixtures.

N_1 is readily gotten from the partial pressures. Thus, at $N_1 = 0.531$, at 90°, we calculate

$$p_1 = p_1^\circ N_1 = 0.531 \times 1112 = 590 \text{ mm.}$$

and the mol fraction of CCl_4 in the vapor, or distillate, is $590/760 = 0.777$. Similar calculations yield the other figures given in the last row of the table, and which are plotted in the upper curve of Fig. 2.

Conversely, if the boiling point-composition curve is known, it is possible to determine whether a mixture obeys Raoult's law, for the values of p_1°, p_2° and N_1 should give the pressure under which the mixture boils when substituted in Equation 2.

SOLUBILITY OF GASES.

The treatment of the solubility of vapors used in the preceding section can be applied to any gas below its critical temperatures as has been shown by Dolezalek.[1] However, the saturation pressure of the gas is high for many of the gases with which we may wish to deal, and the deviations of the gas from the ideal gas laws may be considerable. In such a case it is possible, where the necessary data are available, to calculate the fugacity of the gas instead of its vapor pressure by the method outlined in Chapter III [2] but it will not ordinarily be worth while to do so, since the deviations from Raoult's law

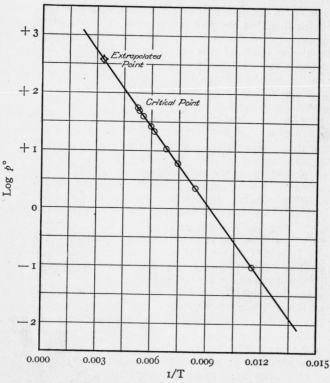

Fig. 3.—Vapor Pressures of Methane.

are usually so large as to outweigh those resulting from the use of pressures instead of fugacities.

If the gas is above its critical temperature, $p°$ ceases to have any meaning as a saturation pressure, but by extrapolating the vapor pressure above the critical temperature a fictitious value of $p°$ can be obtained which can be used for an approximate calculation of the

[1] Dolezalek, *Z. physik. chem.,* **71,** 191 (1910).
[2] Dolezalek has attempted to correct for the departure from the ideal gas laws by using $p + a/v^2$ in place of p. This is not sufficient, however, to give what he calls the "reduced pressure" of a perfect gas, for the term a/v^2 does not account for the entire departure.

solubility of the gas. This extrapolation can be more conveniently made by plotting log $p°$ against $1/T$, for according to the Clausius-Clapeyron equation this should give a nearly linear plot. This is evident if we transform the equation as usually written,

$$2.3\, \frac{d \log p°}{dT} = \frac{L}{RT^2}, \text{ into } \frac{d \log p}{d(1/T)} = \frac{-L}{2.3R}. \tag{3}$$

Since L is nearly constant at lower pressures, and R is constant, the slope of the curve should be nearly constant at lower pressures. It is rather surprising that the plot should remain nearly linear up even to the neighborhood of the critical point, where the assumptions upon which the above form of the equation is based no longer hold. Fig. 3 illustrates this plot for the vapor pressures of liquid methane, according to the data of Olszewski.[3] It is a simple matter to extrapolate to 25° C., which is above the critical temperature, — 95.5°, and where log $p° = 2.56$, and $p° = 370$ atm. This value may be used to calculate N in the equation $N = p/p°$. Letting $p = 1$, to get the solubility of methane in any solvent when the partial pressure of the methane above the solution is one atmosphere, we have $N = 1/370 = 0.0027$. As a matter of fact, this gives the right order of magnitude, for, according to the measurements of MacDaniel, the solubility of methane in hexane, in which we may expect it to obey Raoult's law fairly well, is 0.0031. In xylene it is 0.0026.

Again, we might attempt to use fugacity instead of vapor pressure of the gas, plotting log f against $1/T$, and get an extrapolated value of the fugacity, but for the reasons previously stated, and which will appear more fully in Chapter XII, it is wiser to confine our attention to the qualitative relations that are apparent from the foregoing treatment of the problem, which are as follows:

Expressing the solubility of a gas in terms of its mol fraction, on the bases of Raoult's law:

1. *A gas will be equally soluble in all solvents, at a given partial pressure*, since $N = p/p°$, and the character of the solvent does not appear in the ratio $p/p°$.

2. *The solubility is proportional to the partial pressure* (Henry's law), since $p°$ depends only upon the temperature.

3. *The gas with the higher critical temperature, and boiling point, will be more soluble than one with a lower critical temperature*, since $p°$ will be smaller for the former. This is illustrated in the accompanying table.

TABLE 1.

Gas	Crit. Temp.	Solubility, 10 N₂, at 20°.[4]		
		in C₆H₆	in CHCl₃	in CS₂
H₂	— 235°	2.6	....	....
N₂	— 146°	4.1	4.3	1.3
CO	— 141°	6.1	6.3	2.0
CO₂	+ 34°	94.	123.	23.

[3] Olszewski, *Compt. rend.*, **100**, 940 (1885).
[4] Calculated from measurements of Just, *Z. physik. Chem.*, **37**, 342 (1901).

Gas	Crit. Temp.	Solubility, $10^4 N_2^s$, at $25°$ in C_6H_6	in C_6H_{14}
CH_4	-95.5	18	31
C_2H_4	$+10.$	125	159
C_2H_6	$+34.$	..	171

4. *The solubility of a gas diminishes with increasing temperature.*
The decrease can be calculated from the Clausius-Clapeyron equation
in cases where this may be expected to hold.

MISCIBILITY OF LIQUIDS.

When two liquids are sufficiently alike to obey Raoult's law (cf.
Chapter III) it is evident that they must be miscible in all proportions,
for only where the internal forces are sufficiently unlike could there
be separation into two liquid phases. Suppose, further, that two
liquids which obey Raoult's law did form two layers. When equilibrium is reached the partial vapor pressure of either component
must be the same for both phases, otherwise that component would
pass from one layer to another until the partial pressures become
equal; and since the partial vapor pressures are equal the mol fractions
must be equal and the two phases must be identical.[6]

SOLUBILITY OF SOLIDS.[7]

In order to calculate the solubilities of solids in liquids from the
equation $N = p/p°$, we must remember that $p°$ is the vapor pressure
of the pure solute in the *liquid* state. Since we are dealing with its
solubility in the solid state the liquid is super-cooled and unstable with
respect to the solid. The vapor pressure of the solid is, therefore,
less than that of the liquid, so that its solubility is limited, although
that of the liquid is unlimited, as explained in the preceding paragraph.

When a pure solid is in equilibrium with its saturated solution in
some solvent the partial vapor pressure of the solute over the solution
is equal to the vapor pressure of the solid solute, for otherwise the
composition of the solution would change until they were equal.[8] If
we gradually add the solid to the solvent, its mol fraction in the solution and its partial vapor pressure increase until finally the latter equals
the vapor pressure of the pure solid, $p = p^s$, when no further increase
in either the partial vapor pressure or the mol fraction is possible;
and the solution is saturated. We then have the relations shown
graphically in Fig. 4, where for the saturated solution, $N_2' = p_2^s/p_2°$.

---

[5] Calculated from measurements of MacDaniel, *J. Phys. Chem.*, **15**, 587 (1911).
[6] Cf. Washburn, *Trans. Am. Electrochem. Soc.*, **22**, 330 (1912).
[7] Cf. Le Chatelier, *Compt. rend.*, **100**, 50, 441 (1885); Schroeder, *Z. physik.
Chem.*, **11**, 449 (1893); also Washburn and Read, *Proc. Nat. Acad.*, **1**, 191
(1915); *C. A.*, **9**, 1570 (1915).
[8] If the solid is so non-volatile that the reader objects to speaking of its
vapor pressure, he may substitute the term escaping tendency or fugacity.

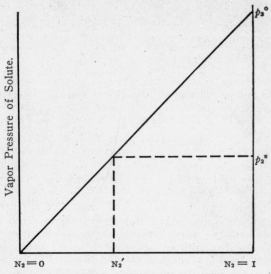

FIG. 4.—Solubility of Solids from Raoult's Law.

The ratio p^s/p° can be calculated as follows. The vapor pressure of the liquid can be expressed by the Clausius-Clapeyron equation,

$$\frac{d \ln p^\circ}{dT} = \frac{L}{RT^2},\qquad (4)$$

where L is the heat of vaporization per mol. The vapor pressure of the solid can be expressed by the corresponding equation

$$\frac{d \ln p^s}{dT} = \frac{L_s}{RT^2},\qquad (5)$$

where L_s is the heat of sublimation. To get an expression for the desired ratio, p^s/p° we can subtract Equation 5 from 4 getting

$$\frac{d \ln p^s/p^\circ}{dT} = \frac{L_s - L}{RT^2}.$$

But $L_s - L = L_f$, the heat of fusion, and $p^s/p^\circ = N$, the solubility, so that we may write

$$\frac{d \ln N}{dT} = \frac{L_f}{RT^2}.\qquad (6)$$

To integrate this equation we may assume with fair approximation that L_f does not change with the temperature, and we may utilize the fact that at the melting point of the pure solid T_m, the vapor pressure of the solid equals that of the liquid, that is, $p^s = p^\circ$, also that $N = 1$. Integrating, then, between T and T_m we have

$$\ln N = \frac{-L_t}{R}\left(\frac{1}{T} - \frac{1}{T_m}\right). \tag{7}$$

Expressing L_t in calories, so that $R = 1.99$ cals., and changing to common logarithms, we have

$$\log N = \frac{-L_t}{4.58}\left(\frac{1}{T} - \frac{1}{T_m}\right). \tag{8}$$

In order to take into account the variation of L_t with the temperature, we may write

$$L_t = L_0 + (C_1 - C_s)T, \tag{9}$$

where C_1 and C_s are the specific heats per mol of the liquid and solid respectively. Substituting this expression for L_t in Equation 6 we have

$$\frac{d \ln N}{dT} = \frac{L_0}{RT^2} + \frac{C_1 - C_s}{RT}. \tag{10}$$

Integrating this between T and T_m, as before, we get

$$\ln N = \frac{-L_0}{R}\left(\frac{1}{T} - \frac{1}{T_m}\right) + \frac{C_1 - C_s}{R}\ln\frac{T}{T_m}, \tag{11}$$

and substituting 1.99 cals. per degree for R, and changing to common logarithms we have finally:

$$\log N = \frac{-L_0}{4.58}\left(\frac{1}{T} - \frac{1}{T_m}\right) + \frac{C_1 - C_s}{1.99}\log\frac{T}{T_m}. \tag{12}$$

To illustrate the use of these equations we may calculate the solubility of naphthalene. According to Bogojawlenski [9] the heat of fusion is 4,440 cals. per mol; the molal specific heat of the liquid is 56.6 cals. per degree, and that of the solid (extrapolated to 80°) is 51.8 cals. per degree. The melting point is 80.05°. ($T_m = 353$.) Using Equation 8 we obtain for the solubility at 25° C. ($T = 298$),

$$\log N = \frac{-4,440}{4.58}\left(\frac{1}{298} - \frac{1}{353}\right) = -0.507 = \bar{1}.493,$$

and $N = 0.311$.

To use the more accurate Equation 12, we first find L_0 from Equation 9 to be

$$L_0 = 4,440 - (56.6 - 51.8)\,353 = 2745.$$

Substituting in 12,

$$\log N = \frac{-2,745}{4.58}\left(\frac{1}{298} - \frac{1}{353}\right) + \frac{4.8}{1.99}\log\frac{298}{353} = -0.491 = \bar{1}.509,$$

[9] *Chem. Zentr.*, 5, 9², 945 (1905).

and $N = 0.323$, a value slightly higher than the one yielded by the less accurate formula. The agreement of this figure with experimental values will be discussed in Chapter XIV.

Some very useful qualitative rules can be deduced from Equation 8.

1. *The solubility of a given solid is greater the higher the temperature.* This fact is too well known to need illustration. Only occasionally do we find the reverse, and such cases, as we will find later, involve a wide departure from Raoult's law.

2. *A solid having a higher melting point is less soluble at a given temperature than one having a lower melting point,*[10] provided the heats of fusion are not notably different in the two cases. Abundant illustration of this might be given, but the following table will suffice for the present.

TABLE 2.

Solute	Melting Point	Solubility, mol fraction at 25°, in	
		Ether	Benzene
Anthraquinone	282°	0.00037	0.0013
Anthracene	217°	0.0059	0.0081
Phenanthrene	100°	0.151	0.207
p-Dibromobenzene	87°	0.183	0.217
Naphthalene	80°	....	0.290

3. *If two solutes have equal melting points the one with the greater heat of fusion will be less soluble.* (This rule will seldom be found very useful on account of lack of data.)

The relation shown in Equation 8 is capable of very simple and useful graphic representation. If we plot log N against $1/T$ a nearly straight line (the curvature given by Equation 12) is obtained whenever Raoult's law is obeyed. The slope of this line is $L_f/4.58$. Its upper limit is log $N = 0$ when $T = T_m$. If the melting point of the solute is known, together with a single point on the solubility curve, a straight line drawn through these two points will give very closely the solubility at other temperatures. If the heat of fusion of the solute is known it may be used to give the slope of the line and hence the solubility curve.

OTHER SOLUBILITY RELATIONS.

There are a number of phenomena closely related to those just considered. For example, the equation for the boiling point-composition curve with a non-volatile solute is widely used for the determination of the molecular weight of the solute, and similarly, the equation for the solubility of a solid developed in the preceding section becomes the equation for the lowering of the freezing point by exchanging the rôles of the solvent and solute. These phenomena, however, together with others, such as the mass law, the e.m.f. of con-

[10] Lavoisier, Traité elementaire de chimie, Tom. II, Partie III, p. 104 (1793). Carnelly, *Phil. Mag.* [5], 13, 180 (1878).

centration cells, fractional crystallization, etc., are of interest from the standpoint of the present work chiefly in connection with the frequent deviations from Raoult's law, so that their consideration will be postponed to later chapters.

Chapter V.

Deviations from Raoult's Law.

In the case of binary mixtures the deviations from Raoult's law which are brought to light by experiment can be grouped according

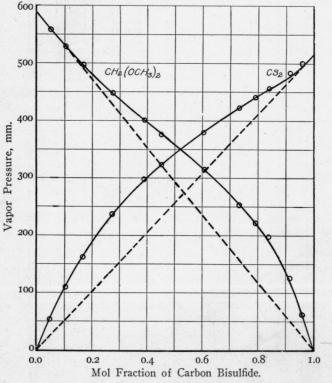

FIG. 1.—Partial Vapor Pressures Carbondisulfide—Methylal Mixtures.

to several main types. Fig. 1, which represents graphically the partial vapor pressures of mixtures of carbon disulfide and methylal according to Zawidzki,[1] serves to illustrate a type of binary mixture fre-

[1] Zawidzki, Z. physik. Chem., 35, 129 (1900).

40

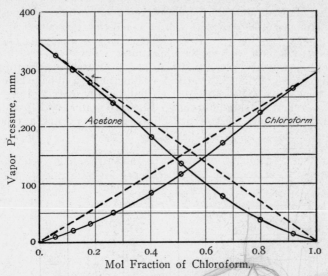

FIG. 2.—Partial Vapor Pressures of Acetone—Chloroform Mixtures.

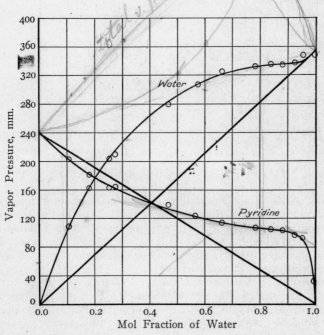

FIG. 3.—Vapor Pressures of Pyridine—Water Mixtures.

quently encountered, and which we may refer to as showing a positive deviation from Raoult's law. It will be noted that the curves for the two components are nearly identical, and that each approaches the straight line of Raoult's law at the upper limit.

In Fig. 2, which represents the vapor pressures of chloroform-acetone mixtures, also by Zawidzki,[1] is illustrated a type where the deviation is negative. It is rare that we find both positive and negative deviations occurring simultaneously, as with water and pyridine,[1] shown in Fig. 3. In electrolytic solutions there occurs a type of

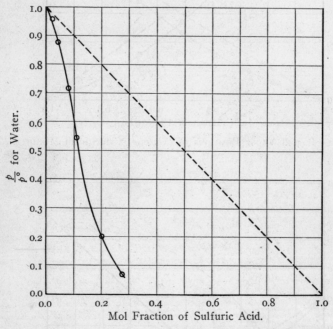

FIG. 4.—Vapor Pressure of Water from Sulfuric Acid Solutions.

deviation in which, if we calculate mol fractions without reference to dissociation or association, Raoult's law is not approached at the upper end of the curve as it is with the preceding types. This is illustrated by the system $H_2O - H_2SO_4$. In Fig. 4 are plotted the vapor pressure ratios of water, $p_1/p_1{}^\circ$, from sulphuric acid solutions, according to the measurements of Brönsted.[2]

In considering a deviation from any relationship it is usually enlightening to examine the deviation itself by a graphic method. There are various ways in which this might be done in the present instance. Thus we might plot against N the difference $p/p^\circ - $ N,

[2] Brönsted, Z. physik. Chem., 68, 693 (1910).

getting a curve whose form is evident by inspection of Figs. 1-4. However, the deviation considered in this way is neither a very simple function nor does it have much physical significance. On the other hand the *ratio* of $p/p°$ to N does have an important significance, since it focuses attention on the second part of the general problem of solutions as outlined in Chapters I and III. The escaping tendency of one component of a solution may be expected to depend first, upon

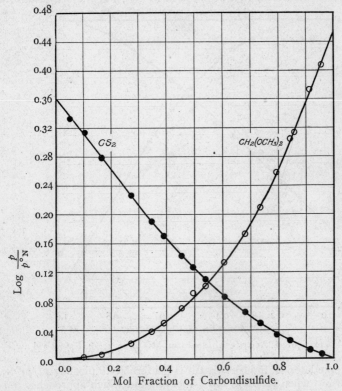

Fig. 5.—Deviation of Carbondisulfide—Methylal Mixtures from Raoult's Law.

the composition, and second, upon the nature of the molecules present. Raoult's law is the answer to the first question, and we now wish to examine the effect of change in molecular environment apart from composition. Since f_1 is the fugacity of X_1 in a solution in which only the fraction N_1 of the molecules are of this species, we may regard the function $f_1/f_1°N_1$ as the ratio of the escaping tendency of a *single molecule* of X_1 from the solution to its escaping tendency from the pure liquid X_1. This ratio is 1 where the intermolecular forces do not change with the composition, i.e., where Raoult's law holds, but becomes either greater or less than 1 when the presence of the second component causes the molecule of X_1 to be held by weaker or stronger forces respectively. Moreover, we would expect this deviation to become gradually greater the more the mixture varies from X_1 in composition.

By plotting $p/p°N - 1$ against N, simple curves of a roughly parabolic type are obtained. We might express this deviation for X_1 empirically by some function of N_2 such as N_2^x, but the operations we

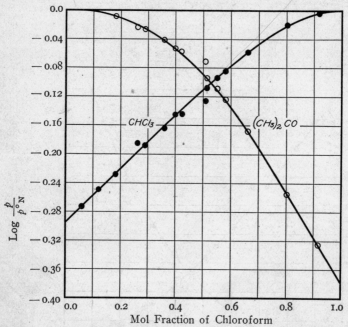

FIG. 6.—Deviation of Acetone-Chloroform Mixtures from Raoult's Law.

will undertake later on indicate that it is preferable to plot $\log p_1/p_1°N_1$, which is also o when Raoult's law is obeyed and which approaches o as N_2 approaches o, giving curves which may likewise be expressed as simple functions of N_2, as seen in Figs. 5 and 6.

Expressed in this way, the deviations are closely related to the excess free energy of the substance in the actual solution over that which it would have in the ideal solution of the same composition. Subtracting Equation III-18 from III-17 gives the excess free energy possessed by X_1 in the actual over the ideal solution,

$$\Delta_{F_1} - \Delta_{F_{1,i}} = RT \ln f_1/f_1° \; N_1, \tag{1}$$

and

$$\log f_1/f_1°N_1 = \frac{\Delta_{F_1} - \Delta_{F_{1,i}}}{2.3 \, RT}. \tag{2}$$

An empirical expression for the deviation will be found very useful, and we may therefore consider two that have been found suited for the purpose. The form of the curves in Figs. 5 and 6 suggests series in powers of N_1 and N_2 such as proposed by Margules[3]:

$$\ln f_1/f_1°N_1 = \alpha_1 N_2 + \tfrac{1}{2}\beta_1 N_2^2 + \tfrac{1}{3}\gamma_1 N_2^3 + \ldots, \qquad (3)$$

$$\ln f_2/f_2°N_2 = \alpha_2 N_1 + \tfrac{1}{2}\beta_2 N_1^2 + \tfrac{1}{3}\gamma_2 N_1^3 + \ldots \qquad (4)$$

Positive deviations from Raoult's law would be expressed by positive values of α, β and γ, and vice versa.

Van Laar[4] has given an expression for the general behavior of liquid mixtures which he derived from theoretical considerations to be referred to later, but which we may present here simply as an empirical equation which has proven very useful for this purpose,[5]

$$\ln f_1/f_1°N_1 = \frac{\alpha_1 N_2^2}{(N_2 + \beta_1 N_1)^2}. \qquad (5)$$

This expression becomes simpler if we put r_1 from Equation II-1 in place of N_1 and N_2 in the exponent, giving

$$\ln f_1/f_1°N_1 = \frac{\alpha_1}{(1 + \beta_1 r_1)^2}. \qquad (6)$$

For the other component we then have the symmetrical expression:

$$\ln f_2/f_2°N_2 = \frac{\alpha_2}{(1 + \beta_2 r_2)^2}. \qquad (7)$$

We will now turn to a relation which gives important information regarding the constants in Equations 3 to 7.

THE DUHEM EQUATION AND ITS CONSEQUENCES.

There is a thermodynamic relation connecting the fugacities of the various components of a solution which not only serves to relate the constants in the above pairs of empirical equations but which furnishes a valuable check upon any theoretical treatment of solutions. This relation was discovered by Duhem[6] and may be written

$$n_1 d\ln f_1 + n_2 d\ln f_2 + n_3 d\ln f_3 + \ldots = 0, \qquad (8)$$

or, by dividing through by

$$n_1 + n_2 + n_3 + \ldots, \quad \text{(Equation II-4)}$$

$$N_1 d\ln f_1 + N_2 d\ln f_2 + N_3 d\ln f_3 + \ldots = 0. \qquad (9)$$

---

[3] Margules, *Sitzungsber, Wien. Akad.* [2], **104**, 1243 (1895). The equations were made still more elastic by the addition of exponents to N_1 and N_2 in the left-hand members of the above equations, but this is probably an unnecessary complication and is here omitted to simplify the later operations.

[4] Van Laar, *Z. physik. Chem.*, **72**, 723 (1910); **83**, 599 (1913).

[5] Cf. Hildebrand and Eastman, *J. Am. Chem. Soc.*, **37**, 2452 (1915).

[6] Duhem, Traité de Mechanique chemique, t IV, Chap. VII. See also Margules, *loc. cit.*

Since the partial molal free energy is related to the fugacity by the equation

$$\bar{F} = RT \ln f, \tag{10}$$

we may write

$$n_1 d\bar{F}_1 + n_2 d\bar{F}_2 + n_3 d\bar{F}_3 + \ \ldots \ldots = 0, \tag{11}$$

or

$$N_1 d\bar{F}_1 + N_2 d\bar{F}_2 + N_3 d\bar{F}_3 + \ \ldots \ldots = 0. \tag{12}$$

Where two components only are concerned Equation 9 may be transformed as follows:

$$N_1 \frac{d \ln f_1}{dN_1} + N_2 \frac{d \ln f_2}{dN_1} = 0; \tag{13}$$

and since $dN_1 = - dN_2$ (from Equation II-3),

$$N_1 \frac{d \ln f_1}{dN_1} = N_2 \frac{d \ln f_2}{dN_2}, \tag{14}$$

or

$$\frac{d \ln f_1}{d \ln N_1} = \frac{d \ln f_2}{d \ln N_2}. \tag{15}$$

Since, by Equation III-19, $d \ln a_1 = d \ln f_1$, $d \ln a_2 = d \ln f_2$, etc., the fugacity, f, may be replaced by the activity, a, wherever it occurs in the above equations, giving, for example,

$$N_1 d \ln a_1 + N_2 d \ln a_2 + N_3 d \ln a_3 + \ldots = 0. \tag{16}$$

The Duhem equation, in whatever form it is used, yields several important consequences.

1. *If Raoult's law holds throughout the whole range of composition for one component of a binary mixture it holds for the other,* for if X_1 obeys Raoult's law, we have, by Equation III-16,

$$\frac{d \ln f_1}{d \ln N_1} = 1,$$

and therefore, by Equation 15,

$$\frac{d \ln f_2}{d \ln N_2} = 1,$$

or, integrating,

$$\ln f_2 = \ln N_2 + \ln k_2,$$

where k_2 is a constant which can be evaluated by noting that when $N_2 = 1$, $f_2 = f_2°$, so that $k_2 = f_2°$, and we can write

$$f_2 = f_2° N_2,$$

which is Raoult's law for the second component.

2. *If Raoult's law holds for the solvent in dilute solution only, Henry's law holds for the solute in dilute solution only.* In this case, as in the preceding one, we can deduce that for the solute, X_2,

$$\ln f_2 = \ln N_2 + \ln k_2,$$

but since this is supposed to hold only in the region where N_1 approaches I, and not when N_2 approaches I, we cannot evaluate the constant but can only write

$$f_2 = k_2 N_2,$$

which is Henry's law for the solute.

3. *When Henry's law holds for the solute in dilute solution, Raoult's law holds for the solvent in dilute solution.*[7] Henry's law for the solute being $f_2 = f_2{}^\circ k_2$, we get, on differentiating, the same expression as is yielded by Raoult's law, and the reasoning used in case I, can be repeated with interchange of subscripts, giving

$$f_1 = f_1{}^\circ N_1.$$

4. *When the fugacity-composition curve is known for one component of a binary mixture it can be determined for the other.* Either an analytic or a graphic method can be used. To illustrate the former let us suppose that the constants α_1, β_1, γ_1 . . . . in Equation 3, have been chosen so as to fit the experimental data for one component of a given binary mixture and that we wish to evaluate the constants, α_2, β_2, γ_2, ... in Equation 4 for the other component. In order to apply the Duhem equation in the form given in Equation 13 we differentiate Equations 3 and 4 with respect to N_1, multiply them by N_1 and N_2 respectively, and replace N_2 wherever it occurs by $I - N_1$. We then have the equations

$$N_1 \frac{d \ln f_1}{dN_1} = I - \alpha_1 N_1 - \beta_1 N_1 + \beta_1 N_1{}^2 - \gamma_1 N_1 + 2\gamma_1 N_1{}^2 - \gamma_1 N_1{}^3,$$

$$N_2 \frac{d \ln f_2}{dN_1} = - I + \alpha_2 - \alpha_2 N_1 + \beta_2 N_1 - \beta_2 N_1{}^2 + \gamma_2 N_1{}^2 - \gamma_2 N_1{}^3.$$

Adding these and collecting terms gives

$$0 = \alpha_2 - N_1 (\alpha_1 + \beta_1 + \alpha_2 - \beta_2 + \gamma_1) + N_1{}^2 (\beta_1 + 2\gamma_1 - \beta_2 + \gamma_2) - N_1{}^3 (\gamma_1 + \gamma_2).$$

Since this is true when $N_1 = 0$, we can set the various coefficients of N_1 equal to 0, getting the simultaneous equations:

$$\alpha_2 = 0,$$

$$\alpha_1 + \beta_1 + \alpha_2 - \beta_2 + \gamma_1 = 0,$$

$$\beta_1 + 2\gamma_1 - \beta_2 + \gamma_2 = 0,$$

$$\gamma_1 + \gamma_2 = 0.$$

Solving for β_2 and γ_2 gives

$$\beta_2 = \beta_1 + \gamma_1,$$

$$\gamma_2 = - \gamma_1,$$

[7] Story, *Z. physik. Chem.*, **71**, 129 (1910).

from which we see also that

$$\alpha_1 = 0.$$

Equations 3 and 4 thus become, respectively, omitting powers of N higher than the third,

$$\ln f_1 = \ln f_1{}^\circ + \ln N_1 + \tfrac{1}{2}\,\beta_1 N_2{}^2 + \tfrac{1}{3}\,\gamma_1 N_2{}^3, \qquad (17)$$

$$\ln f_2 = \ln f_2{}^\circ + \ln N_2 + \tfrac{1}{2}\,(\beta_1 + \gamma_1) N_1{}^2 + \tfrac{1}{3}\,\gamma_1 N_1{}^3. \qquad (18)$$

In order to make these equations symmetrical, as we might expect them to be in many cases, we would have to make $\gamma_1 = 0$, yielding

$$\ln f_1 = \ln f_1{}^\circ + \ln N_1 + \tfrac{1}{2}\,\beta_1 N_2{}^2, \qquad (19)$$

$$\ln f_2 = \ln f_2{}^\circ + \ln N_2 + \tfrac{1}{2}\,\beta_1 N_1{}^2, \qquad (20)$$

which may, of course, be written in a form more reminiscent of the usual expression for Raoult's law,

$$f_1 = f_1{}^\circ\, N_1\, e^{\tfrac{1}{2}\beta_1 N_2{}^2}, \qquad (21)$$

$$f_2 = f_2{}^\circ\, N_2\, e^{\tfrac{1}{2}\beta_1 N_1{}^2}, \qquad (22)$$

As a matter of fact many systems can be approximately represented by these simple equations.[8] Fig. 7 illustrates the degree of agreement for the solution ethyl iodide-ethylacetate, using the vapor pressure data of Zawidzki.[9] The curve is drawn by taking $\tfrac{1}{2}\beta_1 = 0.19$. At the upper ends of the curve the data are less accurate, and the errors are magnified by the method of plotting.

The constants in the Van Laar equation can be connected by means of the Duhem equation by a process similar to the above which shows that $\beta_2 = 1/\beta_1$ and $\alpha_2 = \alpha_1/\beta_1$, so that

$$\ln f_2/f_2{}^\circ N_2 = \frac{\alpha_1 \beta_1}{(r_2 + \beta_1)^2}. \qquad (23)$$

The two curves are symmetrical when $\beta_2 = \beta_1 = 1$, giving

$$f_1 = f_1{}^\circ N_1\, e^{\dfrac{\alpha_1}{(1 + r_1)^2}} \qquad (24)$$

$$f_2 = f_2{}^\circ N_2\, e^{\dfrac{\alpha_2}{(1 + r_2)^2}}. \qquad (25)$$

To illustrate the application of such an empirical equation to the calculation of the activity (or f/f°) of one component when that of the other is known, we may use the data of Hildebrand, Foster and Beebe[10] upon the vapor-pressures of mercury in cadmium and tin amalgams at $323°$, represented in Figs. 8 and 9 respectively. The

[8] Cf. Porter, *Trans. Faraday Soc.*, 16, 336 (1921).
[9] Loc. cit.
[10] Hildebrand, Foster and Beebe, *J. Am. Chem. Soc.*, 42, 545 (1920).

5

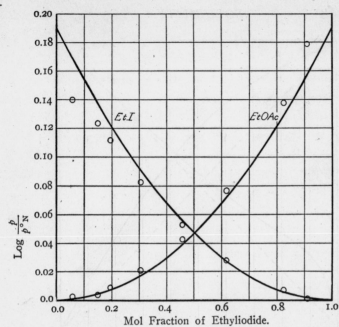

FIG. 7.—Circles Represent Observed Points, Curves Represent Equation.

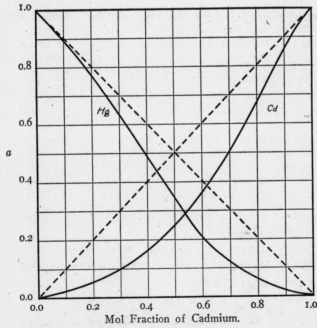

FIG. 8.—Activities of Mercury and Cadmium in Their Amalgam at 323°.

49

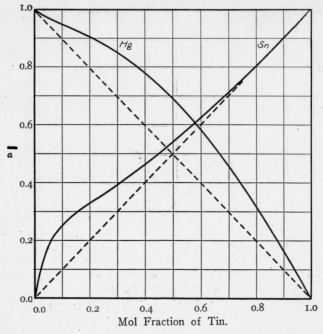

Fig. 9.—Activities of Mercury and Tin in Their Amalgam at 323°.

authors found that these curves were given closely by the following equations:

For cadmium amalgams $\quad \log \dfrac{a_1}{N_1} = \dfrac{-1.40}{(1 + 1.90 r_1)^2},$

For tin amalgams $\quad \log \dfrac{a_1}{N_1} = \dfrac{0.22}{(1 + 0.26 r_1)^2}.$

These give the values of α, and β, in Equation 6 as follows:

	$0.434\alpha_1$	β_1
Cadmium amalgams	-1.40	1.90
Tin amalgams	$+0.22$	0.26

Substituting these values in Equation 23 for the other component, we have for cadmium amalgams:

$$\log \frac{a_2}{N_2} = \frac{0.4343\alpha_1\beta_1}{(r_2 + \beta_1)^2} = \frac{-1.40 \times 1.90}{(r_2 + 1.90)^2} = \frac{-2.66}{(r_2 + 1.90)^2},$$

and for tin amalgams:

$$\log \frac{a_2}{N_2} = \frac{0.22 \times 0.26}{(r_2 + 0.26)^2} = \frac{0.0572}{(r_2 + 0.26)^2}.$$

These last expressions give the activity curves for cadmium and tin shown in the preceding figures.

Equations 17 and 18 may, of course, be applied in a similar manner and should give identical results in so far as the constants chosen in both processes accurately represent the experimental data.

The graphic application of the Duhem equation to obtain the activity of one component of a binary mixture when that of the other is known may be made on the basis of Equation 16. Transforming it into

$$d \ln a_1 = - \frac{N_2}{N_1} d \ln a_2, \qquad (26)$$

integrating, and changing to common logarithms gives

$$\log \frac{a_1}{a_1'} = - \int_{N_2'/N_1}^{N_2} \frac{N_2}{N_1} d \log a_2, \qquad (27)$$

This equation is suitable for the determination of the ratio of the activities of X_1 at two concentrations, but not when N_2 approaches 0, since then a_2 approaches 0 and $\log a_2$ approaches $- \infty$. Lewis and Randall [11] have avoided this difficulty by plotting $\log (a_2/N_2)$ which becomes a finite positive or negative quantity when N_2 (and hence N_2/N_1) is 0.

Since $N_1 + N_2 = 1$, $dN_1 = - dN_2$, $N_1 d \ln N_1 = - N_2 d \ln N_2$, and

$$d \ln N_1 = - \frac{N_2}{N_1} d \ln N_2. \qquad (28)$$

Subtracting Equation 28 from Equation 26 gives

$$d \ln \frac{a_1}{N_1} = - \frac{N_2}{N_1} d \ln \frac{a_2}{N_2}. \qquad (29)$$

Integrating and substituting common logarithms gives

$$\log \frac{a_1}{N_1} - \log \frac{a_1'}{N_1'} = - \int_{N_2'/N_1}^{N_2} \frac{N_2}{N_1} d \log \frac{a_2}{N_2}. \qquad (30)$$

When $N_2' = 0$, Raoult's law holds for X_1, and $a_1'/N_1' = 1$ and $\log (a_1'/N_1') = 0$, therefore

$$\log \frac{a_1'}{N_1} = - \int_0^{N_2} \frac{N_2}{N_1} d \log \frac{a_2}{N_2}. \qquad (31)$$

To make a graphic integration of this equation $\log \frac{a_2}{N_2}$ is plotted

---

[11] Lewis and Randall, *J. Am. Chem. Soc.*, **43**, 233 (1921); also "Thermodynamics," McGraw-Hill, 1923, p. 269.

against N_2/N_1, as shown in Fig. 10, where the data are for the vapor pressures of mercury in bismuth amalgams, according to measurements by Eastman and Hildebrand.[12] The area between the curve and the vertical axis between $N_2/N_1 = 0$ and any finite value of N_2/N_1 gives — log (a_1/N_1) at that composition. A series of values for a_1 can thus be obtained, as shown in Table 1. These values of a_1, for bismuth,

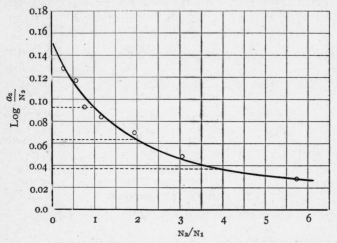

Fig. 10.—Graphic Application of the Duhem Equation.

are plotted in Fig. 11, together with the experimental data for mercury from which they have been thus calculated.

The various curve-pairs given in this chapter, as well as others given by Zawidzki,[13] who checked his measurements by means of the Duhem equation, illustrate the types which conform to that equation.

TABLE 1.

ACTIVITIES OF Bi, a_1, IN AMALGAMS CALCULATED FROM ACTIVITIES OF Hg, a_2.

N_1	0.091	0.167	0.333	0.500	0.667	0.833
a_1	0.181	0.252	0.384	0.525	0.675	0.835

EFFECT OF TEMPERATURE UPON DEVIATIONS FROM RAOULT'S LAW.

The usual effect of increasing the temperature is to cause a system to approach more closely to Raoult's law. This is illustrated for a system showing positive deviations by Fig. 12, which represents the measurements of Schulze and Hock,[14] upon the system benzene-stannic

[12] Eastman and Hildebrand, *J. Am. Chem. Soc.*, **36**, 2020 (1914).
[13] Zawidzki, loc. cit.
[14] Schulze and Hock, *Z. physik. Chem.*, **86**, 445 (1914).

5

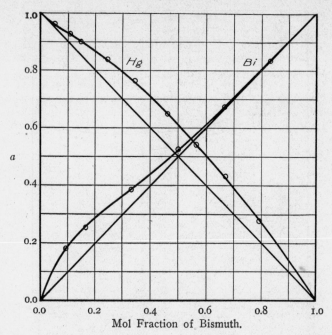

FIG. 11.—Activities of Mercury and Bismuth in Their Amalgams.

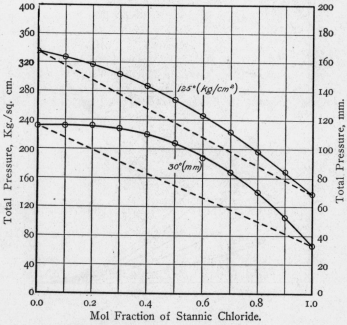

FIG. 12.—Total Pressures of Stannic Chloride—Benzene Mixtures.

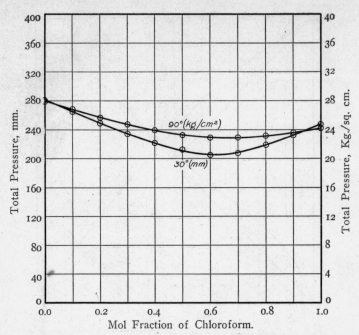

FIG. 13.—Total Pressures of Chloroform-Acetone Mixtures.

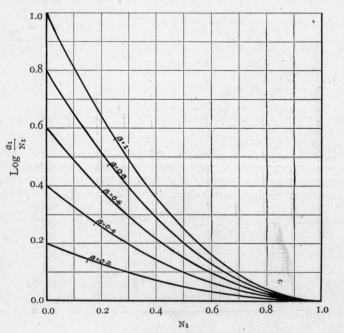

FIG. 14.—Deviations from Raoult's Law.

54

chloride at 100° and 125°. Fig. 13 represents the system acetone-chloroform at 30° and at 70° according to Schulze,[15] which shows a negative deviation, but which likewise becomes more nearly ideal as the temperature increases.

FORMATION OF TWO LIQUID PHASES.

It becomes interesting to examine the effect of continually increasing deviations from Raoult's law. This we may do by suitably alter-

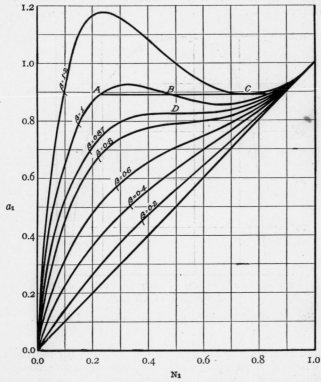

FIG. 15.—Deviations from Raoult's Law. Formation of 2 Liquid Phases.

ing the constants in one of the general expressions previously given. Equation 19, for example, may be written

$$\log \frac{a_1}{N_1} = \beta' N_2^2, \tag{32}$$

where $\beta' = 0.4343 \times \tfrac{1}{2}\beta$. By selecting values of β' from 0.2, 0.4, etc., to 1.0 a family of curves for $\log (a_1/N_1)$ is obtained as represented in Fig. 14. The corresponding values of a_1 are shown in Fig. 15.

[15] Schulze, *Z. physik. Chem.*, **93**, 368 (1919).

It will be seen that when $\beta' = 1.0$, although the curve for log (a_1/N_1) is of the same simple type as for smaller values of β', the curve for a_1 takes on a complication similar to that for the P-V plot of the van der Waals equation below the critical temperature. In fact the physical significance of the present curve is very similar. There are here three values of the composition corresponding to a single pressure, and the mixture separates into two liquid phases represented by the extremities of the straight line, AC, shown in the figure. The broken portion of the curve is not realizable except in so far as slight supersaturation can be attained. If X_1 were added to X_2 the activity

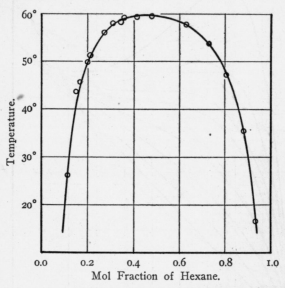

FIG. 16.—Solubility in Mixtures of Aniline and Hexane.

of X_1 would increase along the curve for $\beta' = 1.0$, till the point A is reached, where, instead of the solution becoming more concentrated with a still further increase in the activity of X_1, a new phase is formed having the composition represented by C, which is much richer in X_1, although the activity or fugacity of X_1 therein is the same as in the first phase. Further addition of X_1 results in an increase in the amount of the second phase and a decrease in the amount of the first until it has disappeared, when the second can vary as shown by the curve to the right of C.

The corresponding curves for the second component are not shown in Figs. 14 and 15, but it is evident that, having used one of a pair of symmetrical equations, they would be symmetrical with those given for X_1. If a more general equation were used similar curves would be obtained although not symmetrical for the two components. The ends of the line AC would no longer be at the same distances from the vertical axes, although they would necessarily be at identical mol-fractions respectively for the two components.

As the value of β' is increased the line AC would obviously increase in length, corresponding to smaller mutual solubility for the components, while smaller values of β' would cause it to shrink, finally becoming a point, represented by D on a curve having a horizontal tangent at that point. This corresponds to the critical mixing temperature for the two liquids. In nearly all cases increased deviations

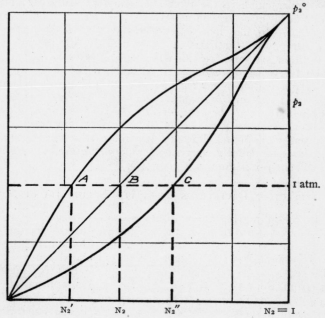

Fig. 17.—Effect of Type of Deviation upon Solubility of a Gas.

from Raoult's law, here illustrated by increased values of β', are produced by lowering the temperature, resulting, when the deviation becomes sufficient, in the formation of two liquid phases whose mutual solubility decreases with further decrease in temperature. This yields the familiar type of solubility-temperature curve illustrated in Fig. 16, for mixtures of aniline and hexane.[16]

EFFECT OF DEVIATIONS UPON THE SOLUBILITY OF GASES.

Having discussed in Chapter IV the rules governing the solubility of gases where Raoult's law holds, it is appropriate to point out the effect upon the solubility of deviations from Raoult's law. In Fig. 17

[16] Keyes and Hildebrand, *J. Am. Chem. Soc.*, **39**, 2126 (1917).

are represented the three main types of vapor pressure curve plotted against composition. We will assume that X_2 is the gas, considered as the solute. When Raoult's law holds the solubility of the gas, $N_2 = p_2/p_2°$, where, as in Chapter IV, $p_2°$ is the (hypothetical?) vapor pressure of the gas over its own pure liquid, and p_2 is the partial pressure of the gas over the solution. If p_2 is taken as 1 atm., the point B in the figure represents a saturated solution, and N_2 its mol fraction, and we can write $N_2 = 1/p_2°$. If, however, the system instead of obeying Raoult's law shows a positive deviation, corresponding to the upper curve in the figure, a partial pressure of 1 atm. will be reached at A, at a smaller mol fraction of gas, N_2', and we can write $N_2' < 1/p_2°$. In like manner, if the deviation is negative, as in the lower curve, the solution will be saturated with the gas at C, at a mol fraction N_2'', and we can write $N_2'' > 1/p_2°$.

The foregoing discussion can be summarized in the statement that a *positive deviation from Raoult's law corresponds to a smaller solubility for a gas and a negative deviation corresponds to a greater solubility than would be estimated by the methods used in Chapter IV.* Moreover, since the usual effect of increasing temperature is to cause the system to approach Raoult's law more closely, *the solubility of a given gas will* usually *decrease with temperature, more rapidly in a good solvent for it than in a poor one.*

Effect of Deviations Upon the Solubility of Solids.

The preceding discussion of the solubility of gases can be applied to solids by substituting for the partial pressure of the gas the vapor pressure of the pure solid solute, p_2^s. In Chapter IV it was shown how the solubility of a solid could be calculated when Raoult's law holds, i.e., $N_2 = p_2^s/p_2°$. We may now note that for positive deviations from Raoult's law $N_2 < p_2^s/p_2°$, and for negative deviations $N_2 > p_2^s/p_2°$, or in words, *a positive deviation from Raoult's law corresponds to a smaller solubility for a solid and a negative deviation corresponds to a greater solubility than would be calculated from the melting point and the heat of fusion of the solid.* Moreover, the usual approach to Raoult's law with increasing temperature leads us to expect that *the temperature coefficient of solubility of a solid will* usually *be greater the less the solvent power of the solvent in question.*

The simple method of plotting the solubility of a solid suggested in Chapter IV, p. 38, may be used to illustrate these last mentioned rules. Fig. 2 in Chapter XIV illustrates the solubilities of rhombic sulfur [17] in a number of solvents, plotting log N against $1/T$. The solubility decreases towards the bottom of the plot with increasing positive deviations from Raoult's law. The increasing slope of the curves towards the bottom corresponds to the greater temperature coefficient of solubility.

[17] Hildebrand and Jenks, *J. Am. Chem. Soc.*, **43**, 2172 (1921).

Chapter VI.

Raoult's Law and Other Properties of Solutions.

When the intermolecular forces in a solution are sufficiently independent of the composition for Raoult's law to hold, as explained in Chapter III, it seems reasonable to suppose that a change of temperature would affect all of these forces in very much the same way, so that the escaping tendency of the individual molecules would still remain practically independent of the composition. No one temperature has any special significance in this connection, and we may well expect that if a solution is ideal at any temperature it will be ideal throughout a range of temperature. As a matter of fact this supposition is in accord with the experimental facts, which show that in general the greater the deviation from the ideal behavior the greater is the effect of temperature upon this deviation.

A similar remark may be made with respect to the effect of pressure. Although we usually find it convenient to work with a liquid system either under one atmosphere or under its own vapor pressure, the properties of the liquid are not at all unique at these pressures, and a solution that is truly ideal should remain so at all pressures, that is, the escaping tendency of a molecule from the solution should be affected by the application of pressure to the solution to the same extent as when an equal pressure is applied to the pure liquid. In order to measure this fugacity we may use a porous piston to apply the pressure to the liquid while allowing the molecules of vapor to escape.

We may, therefore, follow G. N. Lewis [1] in defining *an ideal solution as one which obeys Raoult's law at all temperatures and pressures*, a definition which has some important consequences. It follows from it, as Lewis has shown, that the formation of such a solution will take place from its component liquids without any heat of mixing and without any change in volume.

HEAT OF MIXING.

The heat of vaporization of a pure liquid and the effect of temperature upon its fugacity are connected by the equation

[1] Lewis and Randall, Thermodynamics, McGraw-Hill, 1923. Cf. Hildebrand, *J. Am. Chem. Soc.*, 43, 500 (1921).

$$\frac{d \ln f^\circ}{d T} = \frac{\Delta \mathrm{H}^\circ}{RT^2}, \tag{1}$$

where $\Delta \mathrm{H}^\circ$ is the increase in heat content in the vaporization of a mol of liquid. Similarly, the fugacity of the same substance in the solution is related to the partial molal heat of vaporization, $\Delta \bar{\mathrm{H}}$, by the equation [2] (omitting subscripts to distinguish the components, since the equation applies to either)

$$\frac{d \ln f}{d T} = \frac{\Delta \bar{\mathrm{H}}}{RT^2}. \tag{2}$$

Subtracting Equation 1 from 2 gives the equation of Kirchhoff,[3]

$$\frac{d \ln \dfrac{f}{f^\circ}}{d T} = \frac{\Delta \bar{\mathrm{H}} - \Delta \mathrm{H}^\circ}{RT^2} = \frac{\Delta \bar{\mathrm{H}}_m}{RT^2}, \tag{3}$$

where $\Delta \bar{\mathrm{H}}_m$ denotes the heat absorbed when 1 mol of the pure liquid is added to a large amount of the solution. $\Delta \bar{\mathrm{H}}_m$ for the component X_1 is also defined by the expression

$$\Delta \bar{\mathrm{H}}_{1,\,m} = \left(\frac{\partial H}{\partial n_1} \right)_{n_2}. \tag{4}$$

If Raoult's law holds independently of the temperature $f/f^\circ = \mathrm{N}_1$, which is not a function of temperature, so that

$$\frac{d \ln \dfrac{f}{f^\circ}}{d T} = 0, \text{ and } \Delta \bar{\mathrm{H}}_m = 0. \tag{5}$$

We can therefore say that *when Raoult's law is obeyed by a solution through a range of temperature there is no heat effect when the pure liquids are mixed, and also that the heat of solution of a solid substance is equal to its heat of fusion* [4] (with a small correction for the change in heat of fusion with temperature, Equation IV-9).

It is possible for Equation 5 to hold even when the solution is not ideal but it is unlikely, so that the converse of the preceding statement is usually, but not necessarily, true. We may therefore say that *when liquids mix without any heat effect or when the heat of solution of a solid is the same as its heat of fusion the solution generally obeys Raoult's law.*

Moreover, as stated in Chapter V, we usually find that solutions approach Raoult's law as the temperature is increased, so that when the deviation from Raoult's law is negative, $f/f^\circ < \mathrm{N}$, and increases with the temperature as it approaches N,

[2] Lewis and Randall, loc. cit., also Lewis, *Proc. Am. Acad.*, **43**, 259 (1907); *Z. physik. Chem.*, **61**, 129 (1907).
[3] *Pogg. Ann.*. **104**, 612 (1856).
[4] Schroeder, *Z. physik. Chem.*, **11**, 449 (1893).

$$\frac{d \ln \frac{f}{f^\circ}}{d T}$$ is positive, and, by Equation 3, $\Delta \overline{H}_m$ is positive.

Likewise, when the deviation from Raoult's law is positive, f/f° usually becomes smaller as the temperature is raised and $\Delta \overline{H}_m$ is negative. We may therefore state the following additional rules:

A positive deviation from Raoult's law is generally accompanied by an absorption of heat when the pure liquids are mixed, and a negative deviation is generally accompanied by an evolution of heat upon mixing the pure liquids. The heats absorbed in the solution of solids in these cases are respectively greater or less than the heats of fusion.

Experimental confirmation of the foregoing rules will be given later.

Volume Changes on Mixing Liquids.

The effect of pressure upon the fugacity of a pure liquid is given by the equation [5]

$$\frac{d \ln f^\circ}{dP} = \frac{v}{RT}, \tag{6}$$

where v is the molal volume of the liquid.

If the substance is one component of a solution, its fugacity is affected by the application of pressure to the solution by the corresponding equation [6]

$$\frac{d \ln f}{d P} = \frac{\overline{v}}{RT}, \tag{7}$$

where $\overline{v}$ is the partial molal volume of the substance in the solution, i. e., the change in volume which an infinite amount of the solution undergoes when 1 mol of the component in question is added to it. Introducing subscripts to distinguish the components we may define $\overline{v}$ by the expression

$$\left(\frac{\partial V}{\partial n_1}\right)_{n_2} = \overline{v}_1, \text{ and } \left(\frac{\partial V}{\partial n_2}\right)_{n_1} = \overline{v}_2, \tag{8}$$

where V is the volume of solution containing n_1 mols of X_1 and n_2 mols of X_2.

If Equation 6 is subtracted from 7 we obtain

$$\frac{d \ln \frac{f}{f^\circ}}{d P} = \frac{\overline{v} - v}{RT}. \tag{9}$$

[5] G. N. Lewis, loc. cit.
[6] G. N. Lewis, loc. cit.

If Raoult's law holds at all pressures, as stated above, $f/f° = N$, which is not a function of the pressure upon the solution, so that

$$\frac{d \ln \frac{f}{f°}}{d P} = 0, \quad \text{and} \quad \bar{v} - v = 0, \tag{10}$$

or, the substance has the same volume in the solution that it has as a pure liquid. This is equivalent to saying that there is no change in volume when the pure liquids are mixed to form the solution; for the volume of a mol of solution is

$$v = \bar{v}_1 N_1 + \bar{v}_2 N_2, \tag{11}$$

while, if the volume is additive,

$$v_a = v_1 N_1 + v_2 N_2, \tag{12}$$

hence the expansion on forming a mol of mixture is

$$\Delta v = v - v_a = (\bar{v}_1 - v_1) N_1 + (\bar{v}_2 - v_2) N_2, \tag{13}$$

and if $\bar{v} - v = 0$, $\Delta v = 0$.

We may summarize by stating that *solutions which obey Raoult's law at all pressures are formed from their components in the pure liquid state with no change in volume.*

Since solutions are unlikely to obey Raoult's law at one pressure and not at another we find that *solutions which obey Raoult's law are usually formed from their components in the pure liquid state with no change of volume.* In the next Chapter will be given a theoretical justification of this statement, and also two allied statements that *positive deviations from Raoult's law are usually accompanied by an expansion in volume when the pure liquids are mixed, while negative deviations are accompanied by a contraction.*

The connection shown by experiment between the deviations from Raoult's law, the heat of mixing, and the change in volume on mixing is illustrated by the accompanying table. It will be noted that the three effects are usually related according to the above relations, not only as to sign but also as to magnitude. The agreement is not perfect, however, and theoretical considerations to be discussed later lead us to expect that in certain cases it will not be. In addition to the discrepancies to be found in Table 1 and in a table given by Young,[7] may be mentioned the system aniline-hexane,[8] where the deviation from Raoult's law is so great as to cause the existence of two liquid phases below 60°, and where considerable heat is absorbed upon mixing, there is an *expansion* when a little aniline is dissolved in much hexane, as expected, but a *contraction* when a little hexane is added to much aniline.

[7] Young, Fractional Distillation, Macmillan & Co., London, 1913, pp. 40-42.
[8] Keyes and Hildebrand, *J. Am. Chem. Soc.*, 39, 2126 (1917).

TABLE I.

Solution	Deviation from Raoult's law Percent at t°	Changes on Mixing[19] Volume Percent at t°	Temperature
Acetone-carbonbisulfide	$+35^{9}$ 35°	$+1.6^{10}$ 35°	$-9.85^{\circ\,16}$
Acetone-chloroform	-26^{9} 35°	-0.23^{10} 35°	$+12.4^{\circ\,18}$
Benzene-carbonbisulfide	$\left\{\begin{array}{l}+10^{17}\ 20°\\+7.5^{17}\ 40°\end{array}\right\}$	....	....
Benzene-carbontetrachloride	$+3.5^{9}$ 50°	$+0.06^{10}$ 50°	$-0.69^{\circ\,16}$
Benzene-chloroform	-0.6^{17} 20°	....	$-0^{\circ\,14}$
Benzene-ethylalcohol	$+60^{16}$	-0.01	$-3.8^{\circ\,16}$
Benzene-ethylene chloride	$+0^{9\,12}$ 50°	$+0.34^{16}$	$-0.35^{\circ\,16\,14}$
Benzene-hexane	$+11^{16}$ 70°	$+0.52^{16}$	$-4.7^{\circ\,16}$
Benzene-stannic chloride	$+36^{12}$ 30°	$+2.0^{12}$ 20°	$-^{14}$
Benzene-toluene	$+9^{17}$ 40°	$+0.16^{16}$	$-0.45^{\circ\,14\,16}$
Bromobenzene-chlorobenzene	0^{16} 142°	0^{16}	0^{16}
Carbonbisulfide-chloroform	$+17^{17}$ 20°	....	$-^{14}$
Carbonbisulfide-methylal	$+22^{9}$ 35°	$+1.3^{10}$ 35°	$-6.5^{\circ\,16}$
Carbontetrachloride-ethylacetate ..	$+7^{9}$ 50°	$+0.08^{15}$ 50°	$+0.55^{\circ\,16}$
Chloroform-ether	$-71^{13\,18}$ 33°	-1.5^{13} 20°	$+16.5^{\circ\,13}$
Ethylacetate-ethyliodide	$+10^{9}$ 50°	$+0.7^{10}$ 50°	
Ethylacetate-methylacetate	-2^{17} 20°	....	$-0^{\circ\,14}$

The relation between the deviations from Raoult's law and the volume change on mixing can be shown to be much more intimate, for simple types of solutions, than the above tabulation indicates. The writer discovered some time ago that the values of $\bar{v} - v$, which represent the excess of the partial molal volume of a component over its molal volume in the pure liquid state, are closely parallel to the deviations from Raoult's law as given by the expression in $(p/p^{\circ}\ \text{N})$. This can be illustrated by data for the systems investigated by Zawidzki[20] and Hubbard.[21]

Hubbard gives values of the expansion per gram of mixture Δv, and the weight fractions of the two components in the mixture, w_1 and w_2. There are several methods available for determining the values of $\bar{v} - v$ from these data.[22] We may illustrate by using the

[9] Zawidzki, *Z. physik. Chem.*, **35**, 129 (1900).

[10] Hubbard, *ibid.*, **74**, 217 (1910).

[11] Schulze, *ibid.*, **86**, 309 (1913).

[12] Schulze and Hock, *ibid.*, **86**, 445 (1913).

[13] Dolezalek and Schulze, *ibid.*, **83**, 45 (1913).

[14] The sign is deduced from the effect of temperature upon vapor pressure.

[15] Unpublished measurements by the author.

[16] Young, "Fractional Distillation," London, Macmillan Co., 1913, pp. 40-42.

[17] Schmidt, *Z. physik. Chem.*, **99**, 71 (1921). This writer concludes that certain of his mixtures deviate more from Raoult's law at higher temperatures, but this is because he considers the excess vapor pressure rather than the ratio of the actual to the ideal vapor pressure.

[18] Kohnstamm and van Dalfsen, *Proc. Akad. Wet.*, **29**, 156 (1901).

[19] Additional data are given by Kremann, Meingast and Gugl, *Monats.* **35**, 731 (1914); **37**, 559 (1915).

[20] Zawidzki, *Z. physik. Chem.*, **35**, 129 (1900).

[21] Hubbard, *ibid.*, **74**, 207 (1910); *Phys. Rev.* (1), **30**, 740 (1910).

[22] Cf. Lewis and Randall, *J. Am. Chem. Soc.*, **43**, 233 (1921). "Thermodynamics," McGraw-Hill, 1923, Chap. IV.

method of Roozeboom,[23] there described, which is to plot the specific volumes, or in this case the expansion on mixing, Δv, against the weight percent, as shown in Fig. 1. The tangent to this curve at any point makes intercepts on the vertical axes which represent respectively the values of $\bar{v} - v$, the excess of the partial specific volume over the specific volume. These multiplied by the molecular weights of the respective components give the values of $\bar{v} - v$. Table 2 gives values of $\bar{v} - v$ so obtained for three systems.

If these values of $\bar{v} - v$ are plotted against N, curves are obtained which are strikingly similar in form to those shown in Chapter V,

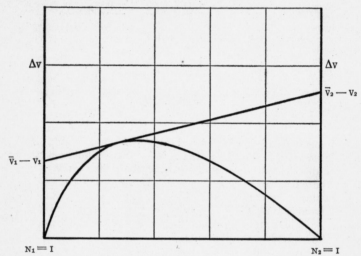

FIG. 1.—Graphic Determination of Partial Volumes.

Fig. 5 and 6, where log $(p/p°N)$ is plotted against N. In fact if $\bar{v} - v$ is multiplied by an arbitrary constant it is possible to superimpose one set of values upon the other with an accuracy probably equal to the experimental error. Fig. 2 gives the curves for log $(p/p°N)$ against N for the system carbon disulfide-methylal, together with the corresponding values of $K(\bar{v} - v)$, where K has been arbitrarily chosen as 0.105. The agreement is probably within the experimental error, and for the other two systems in Table 2 it is even better. We can accordingly write for these systems [24]

$$\log \frac{p_1}{p_1°N_1} = K_1(\bar{v}_1 - v_1), \tag{14}$$

or

$$f_1 = f_1°N_1e^{K_1'(\bar{v}_1 - v_1)}. \tag{15}$$

[23] Roozeboom, "Die Heterogenen Gleichgewichte," II-1, p. 288, Braunschweig, 1904.
[24] Cf. Hildebrand and Eastman, *J. Am. Chem. Soc.*, **37**, 2459 (1915).

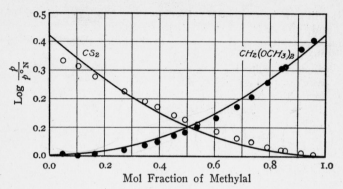

FIG. 2.—The Points Represent Values of $\dfrac{p}{p°N}$, the Lines $0.105\ (\bar{v}-v)$.

where $K_1 = 0.4343\,K_1'$. The significance of the constant will be discussed later.

TABLE 2.

X_1 = Ethyl iodide X_2 = Ethyl acetate		X_1 = Carbon disulfide X_2 = Methylal		X_1 = Ethyl acetate X_2 = Carbon tetrachloride	
N_1	$\bar{v}_1 - v_1$	$\bar{v}_2 - v_2$	$\bar{v}_1 - v_1$	$\bar{v}_2 - v_2$	$\bar{v}_1 - v_1$	$\bar{v}_2 - v_2$
1.0	0.00	3.22	0.00	4.05	0.00	0.31
0.9	0.04	2.68	0.05	3.25	...	0.25
0.8	0.11	2.16	0.18	2.55	0.01	0.20
0.7	0.30	1.61	0.36	1.95	0.02	0.16
0.6	0.57	1.20	0.64	1.40	0.04	0.12
0.5	0.89	0.81	1.00	0.93	0.06	0.09
0.4	1.25	0.52	1.42	0.58	0.10	0.06
0.3	1.64	0.32	1.92	0.33	0.15	0.04
0.2	2.08	0.16	2.50	0.16	0.22	0.02
0.1	2.64	0.06	3.25	0.04	0.32	0.01
0.0	3.15	0.00	4.10	0.00	0.44	0.00

WHAT SUBSTANCES CAN OBEY RAOULT'S LAW AT ALL PRESSURES AND TEMPERATURES?

The preceding relations are very useful and have considerable theoretical significance, but they fail to give an answer to the most important question of all, i.e., what liquids are able to mix without volume or heat changes and without showing deviations from Raoult's law, and how can we predict the magnitude of these effects from the properties of the pure liquids? The heat of mixing and the change in volume on mixing are properties of the solution, and while it is useful to connect one property of a solution with another it is far more desirable to be able to predict the properties of the solution, especially the deviations from Raoult's law, which underlie the whole problem of solubility, from the properties of the pure substances themselves. It will now be shown that the preceding relations make possible a further and important step towards our goal.

We have seen the consequences of assuming that Raoult's law holds at all temperatures and at all pressures. Let us now examine the consequence of allowing the pressure and temperature to vary in such a way as to keep the volume of the liquid phase constant. We may write the following mathematical identity connecting the three partial differential coefficients implied in the preceding sentence:

$$\left(\frac{\partial \ln f_1}{\partial T}\right)_V = \left(\frac{\partial \ln f_1}{\partial P}\right)_T \left(\frac{\partial P}{\partial T}\right)_V + \left(\frac{\partial \ln f_1}{\partial T}\right)_P. \quad (16)$$

Writing Raoult's law as

$$\ln f_1 = \ln f_1^\circ + \ln N_1, \quad (17)$$

(Equation III-12), the assumption that Raoult's law holds at all temperatures can be expressed by the equation

$$\left(\frac{\partial \ln f_1}{\partial \ln N_1}\right)_P = 1. \quad (18)$$

(Cf. Equation III-16.) Raoult's law holding at all pressures is expressed by

$$\left(\frac{\partial \ln f_1}{\partial \ln N_1}\right)_T = 1, \quad (19)$$

while the simultaneous variation of pressure and temperature so as to keep the volume constant, which involves no new assumption, yields the equation

$$\left(\frac{\partial \ln f_1}{\partial \ln N_1}\right)_V = 1. \quad (20)$$

If we differentiate Equation 16 with respect to $\ln N_1$ we get

$$\frac{\partial \left(\frac{\partial \ln f_1}{\partial T}\right)_V}{\partial \ln N_1} = \frac{\partial \left(\frac{\partial \ln f_1}{\partial P}\right)_T}{\partial \ln N_1} \cdot \left(\frac{\partial P}{\partial T}\right)_V +$$

$$\left(\frac{\partial \ln f_1}{\partial P}\right)_T \cdot \frac{\partial \left(\frac{\partial P}{\partial T}\right)_V}{\partial \ln N_1} + \frac{\partial \left(\frac{\partial \ln f_1}{\partial T}\right)_P}{\partial \ln N_1} \cdot \quad (21)$$

Since the order in which successive differentiations are performed is immaterial we can write

$$\frac{\partial \left(\frac{\partial \ln f_1}{\partial \ln N_1}\right)_V}{\partial T} = \frac{\partial \left(\frac{\partial \ln f_1}{\partial \ln N_1}\right)_T}{\partial P} \cdot \left(\frac{\partial P}{\partial T}\right)_V +$$

$$\left(\frac{\partial \ln f_1}{\partial P}\right)_T \cdot \frac{\partial\left(\frac{\partial P}{\partial T}\right)_V}{\partial \ln N_1} + \frac{\partial\left(\frac{\partial \ln f_1}{\partial \ln N_1}\right)_P}{\partial T}. \qquad (22)$$

Now, if Raoult's law holds universally, as expressed by Equations 18, 19 and 20, the second differentials of f in Equation 22 are all 0, and the equation becomes simply

$$0 = \left(\frac{\partial \ln f_1}{\partial P}\right)_T \cdot \frac{\partial\left(\frac{\partial P}{\partial T}\right)_V}{\partial \ln N_1}. \qquad (23)$$

Moreover, since $(\partial \ln f_1 / \partial P)_T$ is not equal to 0, but to $\bar{v}/RT$, by Equation 7, the other factor is 0, so that

$$\frac{\partial\left(\frac{\partial P}{\partial T}\right)_V}{\partial \ln N_1} = 0, \qquad (24)$$

or $(\partial P/\partial T)_V$ is not a function of the composition, and is therefore constant throughout the entire range of composition, and hence the same for the two pure liquids.[25]

It does not follow that liquids which obey Raoult's law *at some particular* temperature or pressure must have identical values of $(\partial P/\partial T)_V$, nor does it follow that liquids which have identical values of $(\partial P/\partial T)_V$ must necessarily obey Raoult's law. What has been proved is that *only those liquids which have identical values of $(\partial P/\partial T)_V$ can obey Raoult's law at all temperatures and pressures.*

It seems reasonable to expect, further, that *since differences in the values of $(\partial P/\partial T)_V$ for two liquids lead to deviations from Raoult's law, the amount of the deviation will be determined, at least partly, by the magnitude of the difference between the values of this important quantity for the two liquids.* That this is not, however, the sole determining factor can be seen from Equation 16 upon substitution of Equations 2 and 7, giving

$$\left(\frac{\partial \ln f}{\partial T}\right)_V = \frac{\bar{v}}{RT}\left(\frac{\partial P}{\partial T}\right)_V + \frac{\Delta\bar{H}}{RT^2}. \qquad (25)$$

The similar equation for the pure liquid is

$$\left(\frac{\partial \ln f^\circ}{\partial T}\right)_V = \frac{v}{RT}\left(\frac{\partial P}{\partial T}\right)_V^\circ + \frac{\Delta_H{}^\circ}{RT^2}. \qquad (26)$$

[25] Hildebrand, *J. Am. Chem. Soc.*, **43**, 500 (1921).

Subtracting this from the preceding gives

$$\left(\frac{\partial \ln \frac{f}{f^\circ}}{\partial T}\right)_V = \frac{1}{RT^2}\left[\bar{v}T\left(\frac{\partial P}{\partial T}\right)_V - v\,T\left(\frac{\partial P}{\partial T}\right)_V^\circ + \Delta\bar{H}_m\right]. \quad (27)$$

If this could be integrated it would give an equation containing volume and heat terms in addition to $(\partial P/\partial T)_V$. A fuller discussion of this problem will be taken up later.

Chapter VII.

Causes of Deviations from Raoult's Law.

INTERNAL PRESSURE.

In deriving Raoult's law from kinetic considerations, as was done in Chapter III, it was necessary to assume that any molecule is subject to the same forces in the solution as it is in the pure liquid; that is, the forces of attraction and repulsion between X_1 and X_2 are the same as those between X_1 and X_1 and between X_2 and X_2. In the first place, therefore, only those liquids are capable of obeying Raoult's law whose intermolecular forces in the pure state are equal. This is quite in harmony with the conclusion reached in the preceding chapter from purely thermodynamic considerations, where it was shown that only those liquids having equal values of $(dP/dT)_V$ are able to obey Raoult's law under all conditions. This quantity occurs in the thermodynamic equation of state,

$$P + \left(\frac{\partial E}{\partial V}\right)_T = T\left(\frac{\partial P}{\partial T}\right)_V, = T\left(\frac{R}{v-b}\right) \qquad (1)$$

where E denotes the total energy of the liquid. This equation is closely allied to the familiar equation of state of van der Waals,

$$P + \frac{a}{v^2} = T\frac{R}{v-b}, \qquad (2)$$

as is evident if we differentiate the latter with respect to temperature at constant volume, when we get

$$\left(\frac{\partial P}{\partial T}\right)_V = \frac{R}{v-b}, \qquad (3)$$

showing that the right hand members of the two equations are identical. It is obvious, therefore, that the term a/v^2 purports to give the value of $(dE/dV)T$. From the kinetic basis of the van der Waals equation it has been customary to designate the term a/v^2 as the "attractive pressure" of the molecules, since the term $P + a/v^2$ is the pressure the molecules would exert if there were no such attractive forces. Similarly, the term $RT/(v-b)$ is commonly designated as the "thermal pressure," since it balances the combined effect of exterior pressure and attractive forces.

The similar meaning of the terms in Equation 1 is perhaps even more obvious. The term $(dE/dV)_T$ represents the energy absorbed in the expansion of the liquid at constant temperature, when the kinetic energy of the molecules does not change, and which, therefore, may be regarded as a measure of the energy absorbed in overcoming the forces of molecular attraction; while the right hand member, representing the increase in pressure of a liquid whose volume is kept constant, may be regarded as measuring the thermal pressure, since the attractive forces probably change little with the temperature if the intermolecular distances are not altered.

From the standpoint of either equation the attractive pressure and the thermal pressure are very large compared with the external pressure under ordinary conditions, several thousand atmospheres compared with one atmosphere or less, and either may be taken as a measure of the internal forces and called the *"internal pressure,"* since the terms of both equations have the dimensions of pressure. There is considerable advantage, however, in using the exact thermodynamic equation rather than the more familiar van der Waals' equation, for the latter is far from having exact quantitative significance, and it is impossible to assign an even approximately exact meaning to its constants, a and b. The former equation, on the other hand, contains terms which are capable of rigid definition and measurement. The term $(dP/dT)_V$ can be calculated from the coefficients of expansion and compressibility, defined respectively by the equations

$$\alpha V = \left(\frac{\partial V}{\partial T}\right)_P, \quad (4) \quad \text{and} \quad -\beta V = \left(\frac{\partial V}{\partial P}\right)_T. \quad (5)$$

for dividing Equation 4 by 5 gives

$$\frac{\alpha}{\beta} = -\left(\frac{\partial V}{\partial T}\right)_P \left(\frac{\partial P}{\partial V}\right)_T = \left(\frac{\partial P}{\partial T}\right)_V. \quad (6)$$

It can also be measured directly with probably greater ease than one can measure the compressibility, requiring simply the use of a constant volume thermometer.

There can hardly be imagined a better indication of the magnitude of the attractive and repulsive forces existing in a liquid than that furnished by these terms in the thermodynamic equation of state, and it is therefore not at all surprising to find, as we did in the last chapter, that *unless liquids are sufficiently alike to show the same values for the terms in the thermodynamic equation of state, and therefore have equal internal pressures, they cannot be sufficiently alike to obey Raoult's law under varying temperature and pressure.*

Similarly, the conclusions reached at the close of the preceding chapter, based upon the quantity $(\partial P/\partial T)_V$, can be restated in terms of internal pressure, since $T(\partial P/\partial T)_V$ we now use to define internal pressure. Deviations from Raoult's law may be expected to be approximately proportional to differences in internal pressure for certain simpler types of system. There are, however, many liquids of approximately equal internal pressures which do not give ideal mixtures, and there are also many mixtures in which the deviation is negative, or, when positive, by no means proportional to the difference in internal pressure. We should, therefore, endeavor to decide when deviations from Raoult's law are likely to be determined chiefly by differences in internal pressure, and when it is necessary to consider additional factors, and what these factors are.

Applications of the van der Waals Theory.

The van der Waals equation of state has been made the basis of a study of the vapor pressures of mixtures by van der Waals,[1] Kohnstamm,[2] van Laar[3] and others. The constants a and b of the simple van der Waals equation are replaced by a_x and b_x for the mixture, whose values are assumed to be calculable from the values of a_1 and a_2 and b_1 and b_2 for the components. These authors show in general that such a procedure gives equations corresponding qualitatively to the known types of mixtures. The complicated mathematical character of their work does not lend itself to a sufficiently brief restatement upon these pages, nor does it seem worth while to do so in view of the poor agreement of the van der Waals equation with the experimental facts. The principal conclusion reached is that the total vapor pressure of a solution should vary linearly with the mol fraction only when the component liquids have equal critical pressures. Since the critical pressure, in terms of the van der Waals theory, is given by the Equation $P_c = 8a/27b^2$, and since b is closely related to v, the critical pressure should be closely related to a/v^2, the "internal pressure." Table I gives the values for the critical pressures for a number of substances arranged in increasing order. By comparison with the tables of internal pressures given in Chapter IX, it will be seen that approximately the same order is obtained except for those substances whose critical temperatures are markedly high or low. If the van der Waals equation more nearly represented the truth, or if the substances considered obeyed the theorem of corresponding states, we might expect the two tables to agree fully.

Kohnstamm points out a number of solutions which obey Raoult's law, whose critical pressures are nearly the same, such as toluene-carbontetrachloride, and benzene-ethylene chloride; while pairs having different critical pressures, such as ether-benzene, chloroform-toluene, chloroform-carbon tetrachloride, and ether-chloroform, show deviations. Since an associated liquid like acetone deviates more from the theorem

---

[1] van der Waals, *Z. physik. Chem.*, **5**, 133 (1890); "Continuität," II, 146 ff.
[2] Kohnstamm, *Z. physik. Chem.*, **36**, 41 (1901); **75**, 527 (1910).
[3] van Laar, *ibid.*, **72**, 723 (1910); **83**, 599 (1913). "Sechs Vorträge über das Thermodynamische Potential," Braunschweig, Vieweg, 1906.

TABLE I.[4]
CRITICAL PRESSURES.

	Critical Pressures	Critical Temperatures, t°
Decane	21	330°
Heptane	27	267°
Hexane	30	235°
Mesitylene	33	368°
Nitrogen	34	— 146°
Carbon monoxide	36	— 140°
m-Xylene	36	346°
Ether	36	194°
Stannic chloride	37	319°
Ethylacetate	38	250°
Naphthalene	39	368°
Toluene	42	321°
Bromobenzene	45	397°
Carbontetrachloride	45	283°
Fluorobenzene	45	287°
Benzene	48	289°
Oxygen	51	— 119°
Ethylene	51	10°
Ethylene chloride	53	288°
Chloroform	55	260°
Nitric oxide	64	— 96°
Ethylene bromide	71	310°
Nitrous oxide	72	37°
Carbon bisulfide	76	275°
Chlorine	89	144°

of corresponding states it is not surprising to find, as Dolezalek [5] cites in objection, that acetone and chloroform, whose critical pressures are 52 and 55 atmospheres, respectively, deviate strongly from Raoult's law. In the later discussion of experimental data it will be shown that the internal pressures, obtained at the temperatures and pressures under which they will be applied, are more reliable as a basis for predicting deviations from Raoult's law than are the critical pressures, which are more remotely connected with the properties of the liquid under ordinary conditions. However, it is hardly to be doubted that an accurate equation of state would correctly determine the basis for predicting deviations from Raoult's law. The van der Waals theory, therefore, while very unsatisfactory from a quantitative standpoint, undoubtedly gives us a correct kinetic picture of the behavior of mixtures in that it relates it to the dimensions of the molecules and the attractive forces existing between both the like and the unlike molecules.

CHEMICAL COMBINATIONS BETWEEN THE COMPONENTS.

If the molecules of X_1 and X_2 in a binary mixture unite to form a compound, such as $(X_1)(X_2)$, it is evident that the number of un-

[4] From Landolt-Börnstein Tabellen.
[5] Dolezalek, *Z. physik. Chem.*, **83**, 40 (1913).

combined molecules of each species, and hence the escaping tendencies of the species, will be reduced. If the combination is complete, only those molecules of the components which are present in excess of those forming the compound will be able to escape as such. If r_1 mols of X_1 are used in making the solution for every mol of X_2, $(r_1 = n_1/n_2)$, the number of mols of compound formed is the same as the number of mols of X_2 taken, and the number of mols of X_1 remaining is $r_1 - 1$. The total number of mols present in the solu-

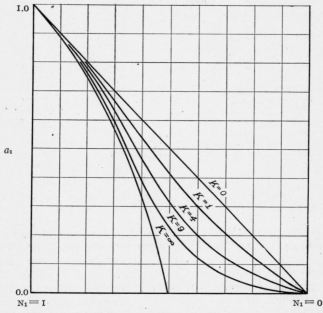

FIG. I.—Effect of Compound Formation upon Deviations from Raoult's Law.

tion is r_1, so that the true mol fraction of X_1 is $(r_1 - 1)/r_1$, and if all three molecular species are sufficiently alike to obey Raoult's law, the activity of X_1 is

$$a_1 = \frac{f_1}{f_1{}^\circ} = \frac{r_1 - 1}{r_1}. \tag{1}$$

If this is plotted against the apparent mol fraction of X_1 a curve is obtained which is shown in Fig. I, marked $K = \infty$.

If X_2 is not completely used up, X_1, X_2, and the compound $(X_1)(X_2)$ being all present in equilibrium in the solution, then the actual mol fraction of X_1 present can be easily seen from the following scheme:

Reaction $\qquad\qquad\qquad (X_1) + (X_2) = (X_1)(X_2)$
Mols taken $\qquad\qquad\qquad\quad r_1 \qquad 1 \qquad\quad 0$
Mols present at equilibrium $\; r_1 - x \quad 1 - x \qquad x$

The total number of mols being $r_1 - x + 1 - x + x = r_1 - x + 1$, the mol fraction, and hence, assuming Raoult's law for each molecular species, the activity of X_1 are given by the equation

$$a_1 = \frac{f_1}{f_1{}^\circ} = \frac{r_1 - x}{r_1 - x + 1}. \tag{2}$$

The activity of X_2 is given by

$$a_2 = \frac{f_2}{f_2{}^\circ} = \frac{1 - x}{r_1 - x + 1}, \tag{3}$$

and that of the compound by

$$a_x = \frac{f_x}{f_x{}^\circ} = \frac{x}{r_1 - x + 1}. \tag{4}$$

These three activities are connected by the mass-law constant,

$$K = \frac{a_x}{a_1 a_2}, \tag{5}$$

and if the mol fractions used in Equations 2, 3 and 4 truly represent the activities, we can write

$$K = \frac{x}{r_1 - x + 1} \cdot \frac{r_1 - x + 1}{r_1 - x} \cdot \frac{r_1 - x + 1}{1 - x} = \frac{x(r_1 - x + 1)}{(r_1 - x)(1 - x)}. \tag{6}$$

This equation can be used to eliminate x from any one of the Equations 2, 3 or 4. Combined with the first, for example, it gives

$$a_1 = \frac{r_1 - 1 + \sqrt{(r_1 + 1)^2 - kr_1}}{r_1 + 1 + \sqrt{(r_1 + 1)^2 - kr_1}}, \tag{7}$$

where $k = 4K/(K + 1)$. When the formation of the compound is complete, $K = \infty$, and this equation reduces to Equation 1, while if $K = 0$, no combination takes place, and the equation becomes the simple expression for Raoult's law, $a_1 = r_1/(r_1 + 1)$. By assigning a series of values to K there are obtained the family of curves illustrated in Fig. 1.

Dolezalek [6] was the first to assume the occurrence of chemical reactions in solutions to account quantitatively for deviations from Raoult's law. Table 2 gives the partial pressures of acetone and chloroform in their solutions according to the measurements of Zawidski [7] compared with the values calculated by the method just outlined, assuming $K = 1.25$.

Dolezalek and Schulze [8] applied the same method to calculating the total pressures $(p_1{}^\circ a_1 + p_2{}^\circ a_2)$ of solutions of chloroform and

[6] Dolezalek, *Z. physik. Chem.*, **64**, 727 (1908).
[7] Zawidzki, *Z. physik. Chem.*, **35**, 129 (1900).
[8] Dolezalek and Schulze, *Z. physik. Chem.*, **83**, 45 (1913).

TABLE 2.

Chloroform		Partial pressure, acetone		Partial pressure, chloroform, mm.	
N_1	r_1	Observ.	Calc.	Observ.	Calc.
0.000	0.000	345	(345)	0	0
0.060	0.064	323	323	9	8
0.184	0.225	276	274	32	30
0.263	0.357	241	241	50	47
0.361	0.566	200	198	73	73
0.424	0.736	174	170	89	92
0.508	1.035	138	134	115	120
0.581	1.390	109	106	140	147
0.662	1.962	79	78	170	177
0.802	4.060	38	38	224	229
0.918	11.15	13	14	266	268
1.000	∞	0	0	293	(293)

ether. Table 3 gives the calculated values, assuming $K = 2.36$, compared with the measured values of Kohnstamm and Dalfsen[9] at 33.25°.

TABLE 3.

TOTAL PRESSURES OF CHLOROFORM-ETHER SOLUTIONS AT 33.25°.

Mol Fraction of Chloroform..	0	0.102	0.305	0.500	0.705	0.920	1.000
Total Pressure {Observed	731	661	499	355	281	270	276
{Calculated ...	(731)	657	500	355	294	276	(276)

The vapor pressures of cadmium amalgams at 322° can be accounted for by assuming the partial formation of a solvate having the simple formula CdHg, putting k in the above equation equal to 3 (corresponding to $K = 3$).[10] Table 4 shows the agreement of the observed values of a for mercury at various mol fractions of mercury, with the values so calculated, in the third row.

TABLE 4.

CADMIUM AMALGAMS AT 322°.

Mol Fraction of Mercury .	0.931	0.861	0.738	0.623	0.488	0.418	0.331
a { Observed	0.921	0.850	0.688	0.525	0.322	0.232	0.148
{ Calculated Eq. 7........	0.928	0.847	0.682	0.513	0.317	0.235	0.154
{ " Eq. V-7......	0.927	0.845	0.680	0.522	0.323	0.235	0.148

More complicated types of solvation can be treated according to the same principles as those just outlined. For example, if the compound formed in the solution consists of 2 molecules of X_2 to 1 molecule of X_1, the equation for its formation, and the number of molecules of each species present at equilibrium would be as follows:

Reaction $\qquad\qquad\qquad (X_1) + 2(X_2) = (X_1)(X_2)_2$

Mols taken $\qquad\qquad\quad\ r_1 \qquad\quad 1 \qquad\quad 0$

Mols present at equilibrium $\ r_1 - x \quad 1 - 2x \qquad x$

[9] Kohnstamm and Dalfsen, *Proc. Akad. Wet.*, **29**, 156 (1901).
[10] Hildebrand, Foster and Beebe, *J. Am. Chem. Soc.*, **42**, 545 (1920).

The total number of mols being $r_1 - 2x + 1$, the activities, if equal to the respective mol fractions, would be

$$a_1 = \frac{r_1 - x}{r_1 - 2x + 1}, \tag{8}$$

$$a_2 = \frac{1 - 2x}{r_1 - 2x + 1}, \tag{9}$$

$$a_x = \frac{x}{r_1 - 2x + 1}. \tag{10}$$

The mass-law constant would be

$$K = \frac{a_x}{a_1 a_2{}^2} = \frac{(r_1 - x)(r_1 - 2x + 1)^2}{x(1 - 2x)^2}, \tag{11}$$

which could be used to eliminate the variable x in the three preceding equations.[11]

Where the formation of the compound is complete, the respective activities become

$$a_1 = \frac{r_1 - 0.5}{r_1}, \tag{12}$$

$$a_2 = \frac{1 - 2r_1}{1 - r_1}, \tag{13}$$

$$a_x = \frac{0.5}{r_1}, \text{ and } \frac{r_1}{1 - r_1}. \tag{14}$$

Such equations become much simpler for dilute solutions where r_1 may be assumed to be very large or very small, depending upon which component is dilute.

The effect of solvation upon the solubilities of solids has been clearly illustrated by Kendall, Davidson and Adler,[12] by a series of curves representing the melting point diagrams for a series of binary mixtures in which there is assumed a gradually increasing compound formation in the liquid state. Their diagram is reproduced in Fig. 2. "In this diagram, temperature is plotted against the molecular composition of the saturated solution. To facilitate comparison of the curves it is necessary to note that the point A represents the same temperature throughout—the melting point of pure substance A.

Curve I indicates the ideal system A-B_1, where compound formation is entirely absent. The solubility curve of A in B_1, the line AC," as well as that of B_1 in A, the line DB, "represents the ideal solution Equation," IV-7.

"The stable portions of the two curves end at their point of intersection, E, the eutectic point of the system.

[11] Expressions of this sort have been used by Hildebrand and Eastman, *J. Am. Chem. Soc.*, **37**, 2452 (1915), in connection with thallium amalgams.
[12] Kendall, Davidson and Adler, *J. Am. Chem. Soc.*, **43**, 1481 (1921).

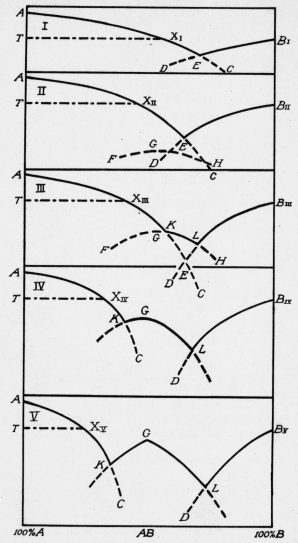

FIG. 2.—Effect of Compound Formation upon Melting Point and Solubility.

Curves II to V illustrate the successive changes which occur in the diagram as compound formation increases.[13] In Curve II the compound formed is so highly dissociated in solution that its solu-

---

[13] For the sake of simplicity, only a single compound of the type *AB* is considered. The argument, however, can readily be extended to other types.

bility curve FGH never enters the stable region of the diagram; in Curve III compound formation is somewhat more extensive and the solubility curve of the compound AB_{III} possesses a limited stable interval KL; in Curve IV this interval has expanded sufficiently to exhibit a maximum point at G (in other words, the compound AB_{IV} is stable at its melting point); in Curve V, finally the compound AB_V is not dissociated at all into its components in the solution, the system consisting, indeed, of two simple systems of the type shown in Curve I compressed into one composition range.

"The essential point to be noted in these systems is the depression of the curve AC from its ideal position, which compound formation in solution necessitates.[14] If only part of the total A in solution exists as uncombined A then, since the solution of *uncombined* A reaches the ideal value, the total mol fraction of A in the saturated solution must exceed this ideal value by an amount depending on the stability of the compound AB in the liquid state. The solubility of A at any fixed temperature T consequently increases regularly as we pass from Curve I to Curve V. This may best be seen by comparing the compositions of the saturated solutions at temperature T (represented by the points X_I, X_{II}, X_{III}, X_{IV}, X_V respectively on the various curves).

"Increasing solubility and increasing compound formation, therefore, for a fixed solute A in a series of different solvents, proceed in parallel."

Association of One Component.

In order to account for positive deviations from Raoult's law Dolezalek[15] has assumed that one of the components is associated, containing a certain proportion of double molecules which are dissociated into single molecules as this component is diluted with the other, each molecular species present, however, obeying Raoult's law when the "true" mol fraction rather than the apparent mol fraction is considered. If we consider a solution made up of r_1 mols of X_1 to 1 mol of X_2 considered as single molecules, the latter being partly associated, however, to form x mols of double molecules, the number of mols of single molecules remaining in the solution would be $1 - 2x$, and their mol fractions $(1 - 2x)/(r_1 + 1 - x)$. The mol fraction of X_1 would be $r_1/(r_1 + 1 - x)$. If the activities are equal to the mol fractions we have, for the unassociated or normal component X_1,

$$a_1 = \frac{f_1}{f_1{}^{\circ}} = \frac{r_1}{r_1 + 1 - x}, \tag{15}$$

[14] In Curve I, AC is tangential to the B composition axis ($N_A = 0$); in Curve V, AC is tangential to the AB composition axis ($N_A = 0.5$). In the remaining curves AC assumes an intermediate position.

[15] Dolezalek, *Z. physik. Chem.*, 64, 727 (1908).

for the single molecules of the associated component, X_2,

$$a_2' = \frac{f_2'}{f_2'^{\circ}} = \frac{1 - 2x}{(r_1 + 1 - x)}, \tag{16}$$

and for the double molecules of the same component,

$$a_2'' = \frac{x}{r_1 + 1 - x'}. \tag{17}$$

The mass-law constant for the reaction $2(X_1) = (X_1)_2$ is

$$K = \frac{a_2''}{a_2'^2} = \left(\frac{x}{r_1 + 1 - x}\right)\left(\frac{1 - 2x}{r_1 + 1 - x}\right)^2,$$

or

$$K = \frac{x(r_1 + 1 - x)}{(1 - 2x)^2}. \tag{18}$$

Using this to eliminate the variable x from Equation 15, we obtain

$$a_1 = \frac{f_1}{f_1^{\circ}} = \frac{2kr_1}{2kr_1 + k - r_1 + \sqrt{r_1^2 + 2kr_1 + k}}, \tag{19}$$

and

$$a_2' = \frac{f_2'}{f_2'^{\circ}} = \frac{-2r_1 + 2\sqrt{r_1^2 + 2kr_1 + k}}{2kr_1 + k - r_1 + \sqrt{r_1^2 + 2kr_1 + k}} \tag{20}$$

where $k = 4K + 1$.

In applying Equation 20 we must note that $f_2'^{\circ}$ is not given by the actual vapor pressure of pure liquid X_2, which we may call p_2°, but refers rather to a hypothetical liquid composed entirely of single molecules of X_2. Writing vapor pressures in place of fugacities, Equation 20 becomes

$$\frac{p_2'}{p_2'^{\circ}} = \frac{-2r_1 + 2\sqrt{r_1^2 + 2kr_1 + k}}{2kr_1 + k - r_1 + \sqrt{r_1^2 + 2kr_1 + k}}. \tag{21}$$

When no X_1 is present, $r_1 = 0$, and p_2' becomes p_2°, giving

$$\frac{p_2^{\circ}}{p_2'^{\circ}} = \frac{2\sqrt{k}}{\sqrt{k} + k}. \tag{22}$$

Dividing Equation 21 by 22 eliminates $p_2'^{\circ}$, giving

$$\frac{p_2'}{p_2^{\circ}} = (\sqrt{k} + 1)\frac{-r_1 + \sqrt{r_1^2 + 2kr_1 + k}}{2kr_1 + k - r_1 + \sqrt{r_1^2 + 2kr_1 + k}}. \tag{23}$$

where p_2' is the partial pressure of X_2 in the solution and p_2° that in the pure liquid.

Equations 19 and 23 can be used to calculate vapor pressures of solutions of the type under consideration by assigning appropriate

TABLE 5.

BENZENE-CARBONTETRACHLORIDE. 50°, K = 0.207.

	Benzene		Carbontetrachloride	
N_{CCl_4}	Partial Pressures			
	Observed	Calculated	Observed	Calculated
0.000	268.0	(268.0)	0.0	0.0
0.0507	253.4	254.5	18.6	19.1
0.1170	237.1	237.3	40.5	40.6
0.1758	221.8	222.1	59.7	59.9
0.2515	202.5	202.8	82.9	84.0
0.3953	165.8	166.3	128.7	128.1
0.5600	124.6	123.8	176.5	176.5
0.6755	93.4	93.1	211.8	211.0
0.7652	68.3	68.5	238.5	237.4
1.000	0.	0.	308.0	(308.0)

values to K. Dolezalek [16] has carried out such calculations for the systems benzene-carbontetrachloride, and ether-methylsalicylate, assuming the second named component of each pair to be partly associated, getting the figures shown in Tables 5 and 6.

Reference to Fig. 3 shows, however, that even large values of K are insufficient to account for the large deviations from Raoult's law that are found with many solutions, such as acetone-carbonbisulfide,[17] shown in Fig. 4, and carbonbisulfide-methylal,[17] Chapter V, Fig. 1. The curves in the latter figure, also, are more symmetrical than those in Fig. 3 when K is large. Möller [18] has derived expressions for more complicated reactions assumed in order to reproduce certain curve-pairs. For example, the solution ethyliodide-ethylacetate is assumed to contain triple molecules of the former and double molecules of the latter, while both components of solutions of carbontetrachloride-ethylacetate are assumed to form double molecules. In none of the systems which he considers, however, are the deviations very large, and the followers of Dolezalek have thus far discreetly avoided such systems as acetone-carbonbisulfide.

TABLE 6.

ETHER-METHYLSALICYLATE. 14.1°. K = 29.

	Partial pressure of ether	
$N_{(ester)}$	Observed	Calculated
0.0	346	(346)
0.021	343	339
0.048	332	331
0.092	316	318
0.151	301	302
0.302	280	280
0.490	206	206
0.770	122	110
0.850	97	72

[16] Dolezalek, loc. cit.
[17] Zawidzki, Z. physik. Chem., 35, 129 (1900).
[18] Möller, Z. physik. Chem., 69, 449 (1909).

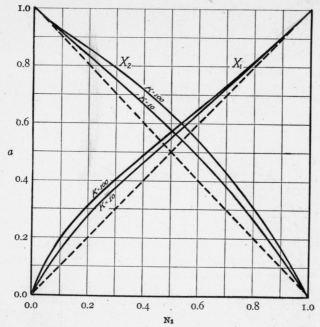

Fig. 3.—Deviations from Raoult's Law Assuming Association of One Component.

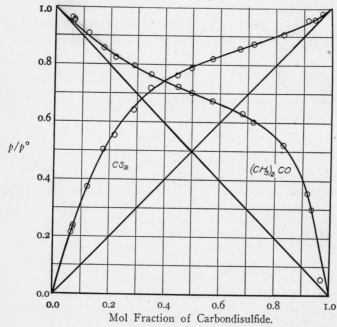

Fig. 4.—Values of $\frac{p}{p^\circ}$ for Carbondisulfide-Acetone Mixtures.

CRITICISMS OF FOREGOING THEORIES.

A still greater difficulty with this type of explanation is presented by mixtures which form two liquid phases. Keyes and Hildebrand [19] who investigated the system aniline-hexane, have pointed out that even the assumption of very complex molecules of aniline is insufficient to account for the extreme deviations here encountered. Fig. 5 shows the known points on the actual partial vapor pressure curve of the hexane, the complete theoretical curve, corresponding to Fig. 16,

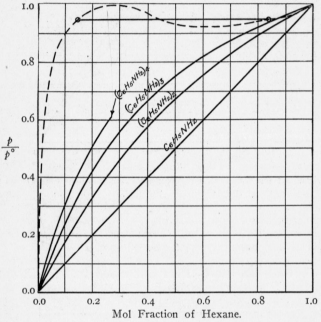

FIG. 5.—Vapor Pressures of Hexane from Mixtures with Aniline, Calculated on Assumption of Association of Aniline.

Chapter V, being indicated as to type by the dotted line. If the aniline is assumed to be completely associated to form molecules of $(C_6H_5NH_2)_q$, where q is an integer, then 1 single molecule forms $1/q$ associated molecules, and if r_2 represents the corresponding number of hexane molecules, the "true" mol fraction of hexane is $r_2/(r_2 + 1/q)$, and the activity of the hexane is

$$a_2 = \frac{r_2}{r_2 + 1/q}. \tag{24}$$

Fig. 5 gives a series of curves corresponding to a series of values of q. It would be expected, of course, that any such complex molecules

[19] Keyes and Hildebrand, *J. Am. Chem. Soc.*, **39**, 2126 (1917).

would dissociate as the percentage of hexane is increased, giving lower values for the vapor pressures of hexane at the upper end than the curves represent, so that the curves represent maximum values. It is obvious that no reasonable value of q comes anywhere near explaining the actual behavior of this or any similar system. If the cause of the behavior lies in the "association" of the aniline it is evident that a very different kind of association must be pictured, an association not into relatively simple complexes which are able to mix with the other component so as to obey Raoult's law, but rather an association of the whole mass of aniline molecules to form a liquid in which the internal pressure, or attractive force between the aniline molecules is so great as to resist dispersion into the hexane.

The difficulty offered by 2 phase liquid mixtures to any purely chemical theory of this sort has been clearly stated by Washburn,[20] as indicated already in Chapter III. Since the partial pressure of each component must be the same in the two liquid phases, the mol fractions, if Raoult's law held, would also have to be the same. It is difficult to see, however, how the mol fractions could be manipulated so as to give such a result.

The advocates of the Dolezalek theory are often led to assume association in liquids which, according to all other criteria, are entirely normal or unassociated. Thus Schulze and Hock[21] explain the positive deviation of the total vapor pressures of benzene-stannic chloride solutions by assuming the formation of double molecules of the latter to the extent of 81 percent in the pure liquid at 100°. At ordinary temperatures this association would have to become still greater. This is in absolute conflict with a large amount of evidence, presented in Chapter VIII, that stannic chloride is a quite normal liquid.

The most striking example of the extent to which Dolezalek and his followers have been led by their enthusiasm for their "chemical" explanation of all deviations from ideal behavior is found in a paper by Dolezalek[22] in which liquid solutions of nitrogen and argon are "explained" by assuming polymerization of the argon to form double molecules!

It must not be forgotten, in considering such a matter, that the fact that a formula which has a theoretical basis can be made to fit the facts by a proper choice of constants is not proof of the correctness of the underlying theory, especially when the formula is very elastic. Although formulas such as 19 and 23 contain but a single constant, elasticity is obtained by assuming *ad libitum,* as Möller has done, other forms of association. It would be strange, indeed, if such a procedure did not yield formulas for the moderate deviations from ideality which have been considered, but while success of this sort may be regarded as evidence in favor of the theory, it by no means con-

[20] Washburn, *Trans. Am. Electrochem. Soc.,* **22**, 333 (1912); *J. Am. Chem. Soc.,* **32**, 670 (1910).
[21] Schulze and Hock, *Z. physik. Chem.,* **86**, 445 (1914).
[22] Dolezalek, *Z. physik. Chem.,* **93**, 585 (1918).

stitutes proof, as has been so repeatedly and confidently asserted. The same system may often be treated by several different formulas. For example, the activity of mercury in cadmium amalgams, in addition to being given by Equation 7, as shown in the third row in Table 3, are also given closely by Equation V-7, using the constants on p. 50, Chapter V, and as shown by Fig. 10, Chapter V, and by the figures in the last row in Table 3. Thus the same data may serve to "prove" two theories which have been regarded by their authors as so utterly conflicting as to call for some very harsh polemic.[23]

Considerations such as these have led the author to a position of considerable scepticism concerning his earlier conclusions regarding the constitution of certain amalgams.[24] The positive deviations shown by zinc,[25] lead,[26] tin,[26] bismuth,[27] gold,[27] and silver [27] amalgams may be explained either by assuming association of one component, or on the basis of differences in internal pressure. The gradual accumulation of evidence on this point is in favor of the latter assumption, while still admitting the validity of the assumption of solvation to account for negative deviations such as occur with cadmium [26] and thallium [28] amalgams. The isolation of a solid compound of thallium and mercury [29] lends rather conclusive evidence for the correctness of the underlying assumption of solvation.

The chief obstacles to regarding the metals as associated to definite polymers, such as Zn_2, are, first, the normal behavior of most of them with respect to the heat of vaporization,[30] and second, the difficulty of making the same assumption regarding the association of a given metal in various solutions. A fuller discussion of metallic solutions will be found in Chapter XVI.

POLARITY.

The above mentioned objections to the attempt of Dolezalek to account for positive deviations from Raoult's law by assuming association of one or both components apply to the very arbitrary character of his assumptions regarding association to definite polymers, rather than to the idea of association itself. It has long been the custom among chemists to distinguish two classes of liquids, merging into each other, as is usual with such classifications. One class is composed of "normal liquids," which have low dielectric constants and conform to a number of general rules concerning surface tensions,

[23] Van Laar, *Z. physik. Chem.*, **72**, 723 (1910); **83**, 599 (1913); Dolezalek, *ibid.*, **83**, 40 (1913). Cf. an excellent critique by Timmermans, *J. Chim. phys.*, **19**, 169 (1921).

[24] Hildebrand, *J. Am. Chem. Soc.*, **35**, 501 (1913).

[25] Hildebrand, *Trans. Am. Electrochem. Soc.*, **22**, 319 (1912).

[26] Hildebrand, Foster and Beebe, *J. Am. Chem. Soc.*, **42**, 545 (1920).

[27] Eastman and Hildebrand, *ibid.*, **36**, 2020 (1914).

[28] Hildebrand and Eastman, *ibid.*, **37**, 2452 (1915).

[29] Richards and Daniels, *ibid.*, **41**, 1732 (1919).

[30] Hildebrand, *ibid.*, **37**, 2452 (1915); **40**, 45 (1918).

heats of vaporization, etc., to be discussed in the following chapter. It includes liquids like the paraffins, benzene, carbon tetrachloride, bromine, phosphorus and carbon bisulfide. The liquids of the other group have higher dielectric constants, and higher surface tensions and heats of vaporization than would be expected on the basis of rules followed by the normal liquids. They are good solvents for electrolytes, and include such liquids as water, alcohol, ammonia, sulfuric acid, and acetone. Salts melt to form liquids of this class.

The evidence, presented at length in Chapter VIII, indicates that the fundamental distinction between the normal and the associated liquids lies in the greater symmetry of the fields of force surrounding the molecules of the former, the field surrounding the latter being unsymmetrical or polar. The result is that the polar molecules have an abnormally great attraction for each other, producing greater cohesions, internal pressures, surface tensions and heats of vaporization, and tending to squeeze out, as it were, non-polar or slightly polar molecules from their midst. The result is an abnormally great fugacity for any non-polar molecules admixed with the polar ones, just as would be the case, to a lesser degree, if the high internal pressure were not accompanied by polarity. On account of the greater selective attraction of the polar molecules for each other, however, the squeezing out effect may be greater than it would be in the case of high internal pressure alone unaccompanied by polarity. The result in either case is a strong positive deviation from Raoult's law with the accompanying effects upon solubilities.

This tendency of the polar liquid to squeeze out the non-polar one is of course balanced by the thermal agitation, which, increasing as the temperature increases, tends to give the upper critical temperature of mixing of two liquids so much more common than a lower critical temperature.

This conception of association differs from that of Dolezalek in that it postulates not definite polymers, like double or triple molecules, but a liquid mass which tends to become one large "group" molecule, as Langmuir [31] calls it, like the crystal of sodium chloride, in which the identity of any simple molecules of NaCl has, as we now know, completely disappeared. The polar affinities which undoubtedly exist in the simple molecule of H_2O, and which are responsible for the ease with which it forms a great variety of hydrates, operate in the liquid state to link the whole mass together so as to prevent almost all penetration by non-polar molecules.

Of course, this distinction between polar and non-polar molecules is one of degree only, the two groups merging into each other, so that we will frequently find it preferable to speak of slightly polar rather than non-polar molecules.

The best known of all rules for solubility, applied almost unconsciously by every chemist, is that *if substances are divided into two groups, polar and non-polar respectively, those within either group are*

[31] Langmuir, *J. Am. Chem. Soc.*, **38**, 222 (1916).

*usually most soluble in the other substances within the same group
and least soluble in those of the other group.* Most of the known
two phase liquid systems, for example, consist of a polar liquid, particularly water, and a non-polar liquid. Furthermore, the polar solvent, water, is a very poor solvent for naphthalene, sulfur, phosphorus,
and other solids of the normal group. Methyl alcohol, a strongly
polar liquid, forms two liquid phases with hexane and also with carbon
bisulfide, both of which are normal. Most salts dissolve in water,
liquid ammonia, alcohol, and other associated liquids, to a far greater
extent than in benzene, the paraffins, etc.

When two polar liquids are brought together the molecules of different species often attract each other more strongly than those of
the same species, so that chemical combination is most frequent under
these circumstances, especially when one species of molecule is positive
to the other in the sense of the dualistic theory of Berzelius, or, in
terms of the modern electron theory, where the valence electrons in
one molecule are attracted to some particular position in the other
molecule. Thus liquid ammonia and liquid hydrogen chloride present
an extreme case of such a positive and negative pair, resulting in complete combination; acetic acid and aniline would show a much weaker
tendency towards combination, while aniline and phenol would do so
only to a slight extent, doubtless insufficient for the isolation of any
definite compound, but sufficient to reduce the fugacities of the components in a mixture. This conception, whose use in connection with
the theory of solubility was merely hinted at in an early paper by the
author,[32] has since been worked out by Kendall[33] and co-workers in a
series of publications with considerable success. Discussion of his
conclusions will be found in Chapter XV.

The connection between solubilities of liquids and their dielectric
constants was pointed out by Rothmund.[34]

SUMMARY.

The following picture of the attractive forces existing in a solution
may serve to summarize the discussion in this chapter and to show the
essential unity of a number of points of view which at first appear to
be greatly at variance. In a liquid mixture composed of the molecular
species X_1 and X_2, we have to consider the forces existing between
the like molecules, X_1 and X_1, and X_2 and X_2, and also the forces
between the unlike molecules, X_1 and X_2. Now if the forces between
X_1 and X_1 are the same as those between X_2 and X_2, and if the fields
of force about two species of molecules are sufficiently symmetrical
or non-polar, then we will usually find the forces between X_1 and X_2

[32] Hildebrand, *J. Am. Chem. Soc.*, **38**, 1462 (1916).

[33] Kendall and Davidson, *ibid.*, **43**, 979 (1921); Kendall and Adler, *ibid.*, **43**,
1470 (1921); Kendall, Davidson and Adler, *ibid.*, **43**, 1481 (1921); Kendall and
Andrews, *ibid.*, **43**, 1545 (1921); Kendall and Beaver, *ibid.*, **43**, 1853 (1921).

[34] Rothmund, *Z. physik. Chem.*, **26**, 433 (1898).

identical with the others, so that the average force upon any one molecule is independent of the composition of the mixture, and hence this follows Raoult's law.

If the forces between X_2 and X_2 are greater than the others, whether X_2 is polar or not, the molecules of this species will tend to associate with themselves, squeezing out X_1 and producing positive deviations from Raoult's law. If X_2 is non-polar, the forces between X_1 and X_2 appear to be some simple function of those between the like molecules, permitting the deviation from Raoult's law to be almost proportional to the difference of the cohesions between the like molecules.

If the attraction between X_1 and X_2 is abnormally large, negative deviations from Raoult's law appear.

This rather simple conception of the various possibilities does away with the fancied distinction between chemical and physical attractive forces. The modern point of view regarding the structure of atoms of molecules sees in both "physical" properties like cohesion and surface tension and in "chemical" properties like the tendency to form "solvates," and "addition compounds," manifestations of the electronic structure of molecules. It is difficult, unfortunately, for us to overcome the effects of the first lecture we heard in general chemistry in which such pains were taken by the lecturer to establish an illogical distinction between chemistry and physics.

The electrical nature of the intermolecular forces was rather clearly conceived by Sutherland [35] while more recently Harkins [36] has presented an excellent discussion of this "electromagnetic environment" and interpreted solubility and other phenomena in terms of it.

[35] Sutherland, *Phil. Mag.* [6], **4**, 625 (1902).
[36] Harkins, *J. Am. Chem. Soc.*, **41**, 970 (1919).

Chapter VIII.

Polarity.[1]

The justification for distinguishing two classes of liquids as respectively polar and non-polar, or associated and unassociated or normal, rests upon a variety of evidence which it is very advantageous to appreciate on account of the very great usefulness of the distinction, not only in connection with the problem of solubility but with many other chemical problems as well.

The Dielectric Constant.

This constant can probably be regarded as the most direct evidence of polarity. When a non-conducting liquid is placed between the plates of a condenser the amount of electric charge that can be put into the condenser before a given difference of potential is reached varies greatly with the dielectric liquid. The "dielectric constant" of the liquid may be defined as the ratio of this charge to that necessary to produce the same potential difference when the space between the plates is evacuated. Table 1 gives values of the dielectric constant for a number of familiar liquids, arranged in groups. The data are found chiefly in Landolt-Börnstein "Tabellen," but include some later data by Dobrosserdov.[2]

The capacity of a dielectric liquid must be regarded as evidence of the presence of polar molecules whose rotation or extension in the electric field increases the capacity of the condenser. The magnitude of the dielectric constant therefore, indicates the moment of the polar groups within the liquid, or the displacement of electrons, or both. The electric moment depends upon both the magnitude of the charge and upon the length of the bipole. Furthermore, the bipole frequently consists not of the entire molecule but of a polar group forming a part of it. Thus the polar character of the $\equiv C - O - H$ group is doubtless very much the same in the higher and in the lower alcohols, but the size of the relatively non-polar alkyl radical combined with the carbonol greatly influences the magnitude of the dielectric constant, as illustrated by methyl alcohol, 32; ethyl alcohol, 25; propyl alcohol, 22; and amyl alcohol, 16. We may regard the electric moment

---

[1] See the discussion by G. N. Lewis, *J. Am. Chem. Soc.*, **35**, 1448 (1913); **38**, 762 (1916); also Latimer and Rodebush, *ibid.*, **42**, 1419 (1920).
[2] *J. Russ. Chem. Soc.*, **41**, 1164, 1385 (1910); *Centr.*, **15**, I, 953 (1911).

TABLE 1.

DIELECTRIC CONSTANTS OF LIQUIDS.

Elements

Chlorine	1.9
Bromine	3.2
Phosphorus	3.9
Sulfur	3.4

Inorganic halides

Carbon tetrachloride	2.3
Silicon "	2.4
Stannic chloride	3.2
Phosphorus trichloride	4.7
Arsenic "	12.6
" tribromide	8.8
Antimony pentachloride	3.8
Phosphorus oxychloride	12.7
Sulfuryl chloride	10
Sulfur monochloride	4.9

Other inorganic compounds

Carbon bisulfide	2.6
Water	81
Ammonia	16
Hydrogen peroxide	85
Hydrocyanic acid	95
Nickel carbonyl	2.2

Hydrocarbons

Hexane	1.85
Octane	1.93
Decane	1.96
Benzene	2.27
Toluene	2.34
m-Xylene	2.37
Naphthalene	2.7

Alcohols

Methyl alcohol	32
Ethyl alcohol	25
Benzyl alcohol	13
Phenol	9.7

Organic acids

Formic acid	48
Acetic acid	6.1
Propionic acid	3.1

Ketones

Acetone	21
Benzophenone	15

Esters

Methyl acetate	7.1
Ethyl acetate	6.0
Amyl acetate	4.8

Aldehydes

Acetaldehyde	18
Benzaldehyde	18

Ethers

Diethyl ether	4.3
Acetal	3.5
Anisol	4.3

Nitriles

Acetonitrile	39
Benzonitrile	27

Nitro-compounds

Nitromethane	40
Tetranitromethane	2.1
Nitrobenzene	36

Aliphatic halides

Chloroform	5.1
Bromoform	4.4
Ethylene chloride	10.5
Ethyl bromide	9.4
Ethyl iodide	7.4
Methylene iodide	5.4
Ethylene bromide	4.9
Acetylene tetrabromide	8.6

Aromatic halides

Chlorobenzene	11
Bromobenzene	5.2
Iodobenzene	4.6

Amines, etc.

Triethylamine	3.2
Ethylamine	6.2
Aniline	7.3
Diethylaniline	5.9
Pyridine	12.4

as exerting less leverage in rotating the molecule of the higher alcohol than the lower.

The symmetry of the molecule also seems to play an important rôle. Thus the nitro group is evidently highly polar, as shown by nitromethane, 40, and nitrobenzene, 36, but in tetranitromethane, 2.1, these polar groups evidently balance each other, leaving little electric moment to the molecule as a whole. This effect of symmetry is probably responsible for the difference between the constants for carbon tetrachloride, 2.3, and chloroform, 5.1, and also for the low constants of compounds like stannic chloride, antimony pentachloride, nickel carbonyl and triethylamine, for one would expect the individual bonds within these molecules to be rather polar, as they are in stannous chloride and antimony trichloride.

It seems to be desirable to distinguish between the polarity of the molecule and the polarity of the bond. The alkyl radicals, for example, evidently have but very low polarity, as shown by the very low dielectric constants of the paraffin hydrocarbons. The polarity found with such compounds as the alkyl alcohols is therefore undoubtedly due to the polarity of the bonds within the carbonol group. Similarly, in ethyl bromide the moderate polarity is evidently due to the bond between carbon and bromine, for the substitution of the more positive iodine, which draws the electrons away from the carbon to a smaller extent, reduces the dielectric constant from 9.4 in ethyl bromide to 7.4 in ethyl iodide. A similar decrease in polarity occurs in the series chlorobenzene, 11, bromobenzene, 5.2, iodobenzene, 4.6, and in many other instances.

This distinction between the polarity of the molecule and the polarity of the bond serves as a caution against relying solely upon the dielectric constant as an indication of polarity in connection with the problem of solubility, for we see that such a compound as propionic acid, with a dielectric constant of only 3.1, contains the polar carboxyl group and may therefore have solubility relations very different from those of many other substances having equally low dielectric constants.

THE TEMPERATURE COEFFICIENT OF MOLECULAR SURFACE ENERGY.

If v is the volume of one mol of a liquid, the surface, if the liquid is in some regular form such as that of a cube or sphere, is proportional to $v^{2/3}$, and the work done against the surface tension, γ, in the formation of this surface is proportional to $\gamma v^{2/3}$. It was found by Eötvös[3] that the rate of change of this "molecular surface energy" with the temperature is constant for a large number of liquids, the "normal liquids." He gave the value of the constant as -2.27 ergs per degree. Ramsay and Shields,[4] on the basis of a large amount of experimental data secured by them, changed this to -2.12 ergs per degree. The relation may be formally expressed by the equation

$$\frac{d(\gamma v^{2/3})}{dt} = -2.12 = k. \tag{1}$$

Most of the liquids which have high dielectric constants and which behave abnormally with respect to certain other relations are abnormal

[3] Eötvös, *Wied. Ann.*, **27**, 448 (1886).
[4] Ramsay and Shields, *Z. physik. Chem.*, **12**, 433 (1893).

also with respect to this one, giving lower and inconstant values of $d(\gamma v^{\frac{2}{3}})/dt$. Since a higher, though variable, value for the molecular weight might be used in calculating the molecular volume so as to give the normal value to the constant, these liquids may easily be considered as containing polymers of the simple gas molecule, the degree of association varying with the temperature in order to account for the variability in $d(\gamma v^{\frac{2}{3}})/dt$.[4a]

Walden and Swinne[5] have shown that this Eötvös "constant" k, as we may call it, really varies with the size of the molecule, and they have given a simple empirical expression for calculating it from the sum of the square roots of the atomic weights, A, of the component elements. Their equation is

$$k = -1.90 - 0.011\Sigma A^{\frac{1}{2}} \qquad (2)$$

According to these authors evidence of association is to be found not in values of $k < 2.12$, but in values less than those calculated by Equation 2.

Table 2 gives a number of illustrative values taken from the extensive tabulation by Walden and Swinne, which serve to illustrate the degree of accuracy of the above relations. We note that even for an undoubtedly normal liquid such as octane the constant is — 2.24, and not — 2.12 as given by the mean value of Ramsay and Shields, or — 2.40 as required by the formula of Walden and Swinne, differences

TABLE 2.

Normal Liquids	Eötvös Const. Calc.	Eötvös Const. Exp.	Associated Liquids	Eötvös Const. Calc.	Eötvös Const. Exp.
Nitrogen	1.98	2.00	Water, 70°-100°	1.97	1.06
Carbon monoxide	1.98	2.00	100°-130°	....	1.15
Chlorine	2.03	2.02	Methyl alcohol, 20°-70°	2.03	0.93
Carbon dioxide	2.03	2.22	70°-130°	....	1.05
Carbon bisulfide	2.09	2.08	Formic acid, 17°-46°	2.05	0.90
Phosphorus	2.14	2.20	46°-80°	....	0.99
Chloroform	2.15	2.01	Ethyl alcohol, 20°-80°	2.09	1.13
Ethyl iodide	2.16	2.15	80°-120°	....	1.35
Sulfur monochloride	2.16	2.06	Glycerine	2.23	1.3
Phosphorus trichloride	2.16	2.10	Phenol	2.24	1.7
Ethylene bromide	2.19	2.17	Benzyl alcohol	2.30	1.6
Benzene	2.19	2.10	Benzonitrile	2.26	2.13
Carbon tetrachloride	2.20	2.10	Acetonitrile	2.05	1.6
Stannic chloride	2.28	2.20	Acetamide	2.12	1.2
n-Hexane	2.30	2.11	Acetanilide	2.39	1.9
m-Xylene	2.31	2.18	Acetone	2.12	1.7
Nickel carbonyl	2.31	2.31	Aniline	2.25	2.05
Naphthalene	2.37	2.29	p-Toluidine	2.31	1.7
n-Octane	2.40	2.24	Nitric acid	2.08	1.5
Dibenzyl	2.58	2.53	Nitromethane	2.16	1.7
Tristearin	5.55	5.53	Nitrobenzene	2.31	2.12
			Methyl formate	2.11	2.04

[4a] For a general discussion of this topic see Harkins, *Proc. Nat. Acad. Sci.,* **5**, 1539 (1919).

[5] Walden and Swinne, *Z. physik. Chem.,* **82**, 271 (1913).

of about 7 percent. Furthermore, a high degree of polarity, as with acetone, reduces the constant only from — 2.12 to — 1.7, or 20 percent. The method is therefore not a sensitive one for detecting moderate polarity. Again, the Eötvös constant and the dielectric constant do not agree in giving any quantitative estimate of polarity; nitrobenzene has a normal Eötvös constant of — 2.12, but a very high dielectric constant, 36; while acetic acid has a low dielectric constant, 6.1, but a very abnormal Eötvös constant, about — 1.0. In general, however, it will be noted that the two methods agree in indicating that water, the alcohols, acids, amines, amides, nitriles, ketones, nitro compounds, etc., are abnormal, associated or polar.

Attempts have been made to calculate the apparent molecular weights and hence the "association factors"[6] of the associated liquids, but the theoretical bases for these attempts are decidedly unsound.[7] Their absurdity is perhaps best illustrated by the data for fused salts in Table 3, taken from a comprehensive paper by Jaeger.[8]

TABLE 3.

EÖTVÖS CONSTANTS FOR FUSED SALTS.

LiCl	0.47	LiNO$_3$	0.45
NaF	0.52	NaNO$_3$	0.24–0.45
NaCl	0.48	Na$_2$WO$_4$	0.64–0.98
KI	1.58–0.41	KPO$_3$	0.91–1.28
K$_2$SO$_4$	0.90	TlNO$_3$	0.81

The values are variable, as with other abnormal liquids, and being small they would have to be interpreted, to be consistent, as indicating a high degree of association. But this is altogether contrary to excellent evidence that the fused salts are rather *dissociated*. The analysis of crystal structure by means of X-rays indicates that compounds like the alkali halides are completely ionized in the solid state. Our reasons for believing this to persist in the liquid state are reinforced by the high electrical conductivity of fused salts. The ions are evidently bound together as a whole by a strong cohesion or internal pressure which resists solution in a non-polar liquid, but these attractions are not selective, they produce no definite complexes, and oppose but little resistance to electrical transference.[9] The only association we are at all justified in admitting is the association of the whole mass into what Langmuir has called the "group molecule," to which we have previously referred.

But while the fused salts cannot properly be considered associated, they are undoubtedly abnormal, and highly polar, so much so that the "poles" or ions are not even connected to any definite partners,

[6] Ramsay and Shields, loc. cit.; also Ramsay and Aston, *Proc. Roy. Soc.,* 56, 162 (1894).
[7] Cf. Tyrer, *Z. physik. Chem.,* 80, 50 (1912); Jaeger, *Proc. Acad. Amsterdam,* 17, 418 (1914); Harkins, Davies and Clark, *J. Am. Chem. Soc.,* 39, 541 (1917).
[8] Jaeger, *Z. anorg. Chem.,* 101, 1 (1917).
[9] Cf. Kendall and Gross, *J. Am. Chem. Soc.,* 43, 1419 (1921), footnote 12.

but tend to be equally attracted by a number of surrounding oppositely charged ions. The salts are, therefore, more or less soluble in polar liquids like water, liquid ammonia, acetone and hydrocyanic acid, and insoluble in liquids of low polarity such as the paraffins, benzene and carbon tetrachloride. The high internal pressure due to this high polarity makes the fused salts even poorer solvents for non-polar substances than water, as shown by the salting out of gases and of organic liquids and solids from aqueous solution by addition of salts, to be discussed more fully later on.

The molten metals, like the fused salts, give indications of polarity, according to the Eötvös method of investigation. Values of the Eötvös constant kindly calculated for the author by Hogness [10] from his measurements are as follows: mercury, 0.10 at 0°, 1.33 at 300°; bismuth, 0.24; cadmium, 0.035; lead, 0.28; tin, 0.29; zinc, 0.07. These small values might be considered as indicating "association," but in the absence of any satisfactory theoretical calculation of the Eötvös constant we cannot be sure that even normal liquids of such very different molecular characteristics should give a value of -2.1. A more satisfactory reason for attributing polarity to the metals is their electrical conductivity, indicating the presence of free electrons. A fuller discussion of the metals will be reserved for Chapter XVI.

THE HEAT OF VAPORIZATION.

One of the best known and most useful of the generalizations regarding normal liquids is Trouton's rule,[11] according to which the molal heat of vaporization, L, divided by the boiling point in degrees Kelvin T_b, is a constant, 21. This quotient may conveniently be called the entropy of vaporization. For "associated" or polar liquids, the extra energy absorbed in separating the polar molecules causes an abnormally large heat of vaporization, and makes the Trouton quotient larger than the normal value 21. It has long been known, however, that there is a trend in this quotient with the boiling point, even for liquids which are undoubtedly normal. Various empirical expressions have been proposed giving the Trouton quotient in terms of the boiling point, such as those of Nernst,[12] Bingham [13] and Forcrand.[14] The writer discovered a simpler and theoretically more probable relation than any of these,[15] i.e., that the entropy of vaporization is the same for all normal liquids, not when the liquids are boiled under a pressure of one atmosphere or any other constant pressure, but rather when the temperature and pressures are so chosen as to give the same concentration or volume of vapor in every case. Table 4 gives values

[10] Hogness, *J. Am. Chem. Soc.*, **43**, 1621 (1921).
[11] Trouton, *Phil. Mag.* [5], **18**, 54 (1884).
[12] Nernst, *Gött. Nachr.*, 1906.
[13] Bingham, *J. Am. Chem. Soc.*, **28**, 723 (1906).
[14] Forcrand, *Compt. rend.*, **156**, 1439, 1648, 1809 (1913).
[15] Hildebrand, *J. Am. Chem. Soc.*, **37**, 970 (1915); **40**, 45 (1918).

TABLE 4.

ENTROPY OF VAPORIZATION AT CONCENTRATION OF 0.00507 MOLS/LITER.

Normal Liquids		Metals	
Nitrogen	27.6	Mercury	26.2
Oxygen	27.6	Cadmium	26.4
Chlorine	27.8	Zinc	26.4
Pentane	27.0		
Isopentane	27.4		
Hexane	27.2		
Carbon tetrachloride	27.0	Polar Liquids	
Benzene	27.4	Ammonia	32.4
Fluorobenzene	27.4	Water	32.0
Stannic chloride	27.2	Ethyl alcohol	33.4
Octane	27.6		
Bromonaphthalene	27.6		
Mean	27.4		

of L/T_c for vaporization at uniform concentration, arbitrarily chosen in this case as 0.00507 mols per liter. This value of L/T_c can be obtained by a very simple graphic method from vapor pressure measurements. The Clapeyron equation can be rearranged to give

$$R \frac{d \ln p}{d \ln T} = \frac{L}{T}, \tag{3}$$

which shows that if log p is plotted against log T a curve is obtained whose tangent at any point, when multiplied by R, 1.99 calories per degree, gives the quotient L/T at that value of p and T, and hence, by the gas law, of the concentration, c. The values in the table were obtained at the points where the vapor pressure curves were intersected by the straight line log $p = \log T - 0.5$, on which log $Rc = -0.5$ and $c = 0.00507$ mols per liter (since $p = RTc$ and log $p = \log T + \log Rc$). It will be seen that there is no trend with temperature of the entropy of vaporization at constant concentration of the normal liquids, although the metals show a slightly lower value than the non-metals. The polar liquids show a higher value just as they do for the Trouton quotient.

The normality of a liquid may be most accurately and conveniently tested by plotting on transparent coördinate paper the values of log p against log T for some normal liquid, and on another sheet the values for the liquid to be tested. A line of unit slope, such as log $p = \log T - 1$ or log $p = \log T - 0.5$ is drawn on both sheets, which are then held up to the light, the line of unit slope on one sheet superimposed upon the one on the other, and the upper sheet slid along, until the curve on one sheet is superimposed, if possible, upon that of the other. If the curve of the liquid being tested is found to have a steeper slope at the same concentrations than that of the normal liquid the former may be considered abnormal or polar.

Like the Eötvös constant this method is usually a less sensitive test of polarity than the dielectric constant, but it adds a simple and direct evidence of association or polarity, data for which are sometimes available when data for the other criteria are lacking. It is also interesting to find that according to this criterion the metals are normal liquids, instead of abnormal, as indicated by surface tension. Evidently the presence of free electrons does not exert a disturbing effect upon this relationship.

A number of empirical relations besides those discussed above add evidence for the distinction between normal and abnormal liquids,[16] but since they agree in the main as to which liquids are to be regarded as normal it is unnecessary to devote further space to their discussion, and we can proceed rather to consider the chemical characteristics of polarity.

POLARITY AND CHEMICAL NATURE.

Having obtained from the foregoing criteria a general idea of the types of molecules that possess polarity it will now be profitable to consider polarity from a chemical standpoint, which will make it possible to correlate the degree of polarity with molecular structure. We have already seen that *polarity is imparted to the molecule by certain groups or radicals, including* $-OH$, $-NO_2$, $=CO$, *and* $-NH_2$. The bonds involved in these radicals are rather highly polar, so that most molecules containing them have a considerable polarity, although in some cases the symmetry of the molecule may prevent the polarity of its individual bonds from producing a polar field external to the molecule as a whole. The great difference between the unsymmetrical mononitromethane and the symmetrical tetranitromethane in this respect has already been mentioned.

The symmetry of the molecule seems to play a very important rôle in nearly all cases. Thus chloroform is more polar than either methane or carbon tetrachloride. Stannous chloride is far more polar than stannic chloride; antimonous chloride than antimonic chloride. The fluorides of the metals are usually among the most highly polar of all substances, forming typical salts, and yet tungsten hexafluoride, whose molecule can assume a highly symmetrical structure, is a substance of low polarity, melting at 3° to a liquid which boils at 19° and is undoubtedly soluble in benzene and other liquids of low polarity. Illustrations of this sort might be multiplied at great length with but few disturbing exceptions.

The polarity of the individual bonds can be correlated with the difference between the positive and negative character of the atoms. An atom of sodium, for example, has little tendency to hold its single valence electron, as shown by the ease with which it is oxidized to sodium ion, as well as by the high conductivity of metallic sodium and the ease with which electrons are expelled by light. The chlorine atom, on the other hand, eagerly takes up an electron, becoming negatively charged. In the crystal of sodium chloride the sodium

---

[16] Cf. Turner, "Molecular Association," 1915. Longmans, Green & Co. Tyrer, *Z. physik. Chem.*, **80**, 50 (1912).

atom has so completely lost its electron that there is no chemical bond connecting it to any individual chlorine atom, it is attracted instead equally by six surrounding negative chlorine atoms or chloride ions. The cohesion of the crystal is thus due to these polar forces, and when the crystal melts, breaking up the regular lattice of ions, the same polar forces remain to produce the cohesion or internal pressure of the liquid.

However, if we substitute for the sodium a metal like silver which parts less readily with an electron, we have in silver chloride a salt which is distinctly less polar and in which the atom of silver shows some tendency to hold on to its electron and thus preserve a true chemical bond with an atom of chlorine. In the typical non-polar organic bond, such as that between carbon and hydrogen, we may assume that the electrons are shared by both the carbon and the hydrogen atoms and that they are not displaced very greatly towards either the carbon or the hydrogen, so that we find it difficult to state conclusively which element is negative and which positive.

The relative electropositive and electronegative characters of the constituents of a compound are indicated by the electrode potentials, and the electrochemical replacement series. This electrochemical character usually accords also with the position of the element in the Periodic Table, the elements becoming increasingly electropositive as we go towards the alkali group, and also as we go from top to bottom of the principal groups. (In the sub-groups, such as that including zinc, cadmium and mercury, the most electropositive elements may be found at the top.) The reverse is true for the electronegative character. *Information is also gained from the relative strengths of acids and bases,* the strongest being those showing the greatest tendency to ionize, and hence being most polar. In accordance with this the alkali halides, for example, would be highly polar, those of silver much less so, silver iodide being less polar than silver chloride. A substance like lead chloride would be moderately polar, while lead acetate would be but slightly polar. The silicates of the heavier metals would be but slightly polar. An increase of polarity would result from increasing the electronegative character of a weak anion by the formation of a poly-anion, for example, a dichromate would be more polar than a chromate.

It seems further, that *atomic volumes have a great deal to do with polarity.* Where these are great there would doubtless be more opportunity for the separation of the charges which produce polarity, the molecule being less compact, and we find, as a matter of fact, that the alkali metals, having the highest atomic volumes of all the elements, give highly polar compounds, followed in this respect by the halogens and the alkaline earths. The element having the smallest atomic volume of all, carbon, gives the least polar of all compounds. The "most normal" liquids we possess are the hydrocarbons of the paraffin series. The difference in atomic volumes may be responsible for the greater polarity of elementary iodine than of chlorine, as shown by the fact that its electrical conductivity in the liquid state is greater than that of chlorine,[17] and also by its greater reactivity. This polarity cannot be due to any difference in the two atoms composing the molecule, but rather to the electron being held under less constraint in the molecule, due possibly to the greater atomic volume as compared with chlorine.

It is worth while to call particular attention to *the small polarity of many halides as compared with that of nitrates and other compounds with negative radicals.* Thus mercuric chloride is a weak salt while mercuric nitrate is not. Stannic nitrate is sufficiently ionized to hydrolyze completely into stannic hydroxide, while stannic chloride does not, and is sufficiently non-polar to dissolve easily in non-polar liquids. This difference may be related to the small volume of a halogen ion compared with a nitrate ion, permitting a more compact grouping which has a smaller stray external field, and hence better resists disruption in the presence of a polar molecule of different species.

The tendency of a molecule to form addition compounds bears an intimate relation to its polarity. The enormous number of hydrates that are known is evidence of the high polarity of water. That of ammonia is shown by the addition compounds it forms with a number of substances such as the salts of copper, nickel, zinc and cobalt. "Ethyl alcohol of crystallization" is known, as in $CaCl_2.6C_2H_5OH$. "Benzene of crystallization" is known in a few cases, while the non-polar paraffins display practically no tendency to form such aggregates.

G. N. Lewis, in his excellent discussion of polarity previously referred to, has pointed out the influence of environment upon the polarity of a molecule. "A molecular bipole of small molecular moment, which would scarcely attract a similar molecule, will be very appreciably attracted by a polar molecule or bipole of high moment, and may form with it a double molecule. In this process the weaker bipole stretches and its moment increases. In general, if two molecules combine, or even approach one another, each weakens the constraints which hold together the charge of the other, and the electrical moment of each is increased.

"This increase in the polar character of a molecule when combined with, or in the neighborhood of, other polar molecules is to a remarkable degree cumulative, for when two molecules by their approach or combination become more polar they draw other molecules more strongly towards them, but this still further increases their polar character. This is strikingly illustrated in numerous phenomena. Thus two substances in the gaseous state may differ but little in polar character, but when they are condensed to liquids the differences are frequently enormous.

"The polar character of a substance depends, therefore, not only

[17] Lind, *Wied. Ann.,* 56 (1895); Lewis and Wheeler, *Z. physik. Chem.,* 56, 179 (1906).

upon the specific properties of the individual molecules, but also upon what we may call the strength of the polar environment. Without attempting to give any quantitative definition of our terms we may plot, as in Fig. 1, the degree of polarity of a substance as ordinate and the strength of the polar environment as abscissa. We then have for all substances a curve of the type shown in the figure where the dotted line represents the highest degree of polarity, namely complete ionization. Different pure substances in the liquid state come at different

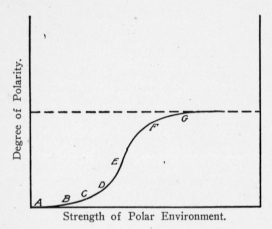

Strength of Polar Environment.

FIG. 1.—Effect of Environment upon Polarity.

points, thus, roughly, hexane at A; benzene at B; ether at C; esters at D; water, ammonia, alcohols, amines, acids between D and F; and fused salts at G. In the last case, since the substance has nearly reached its highest possible polarity, it will not be much affected by an increase in the strength of the polar environment. At the other end of the curve a substance at A in a strong polar environment may move to B, and one at B may move to C, but they would not become markedly polar. It is in the intermediate range that substances are most affected by small changes in the environment. Thus hydrochloric acid, which in the pure state is not extremely polar, reaches nearly the highest possible state of polarity when dissolved in water. Such a change in this region is often much accentuated by the formation of complexes, and thus we have the rule of Abegg and Bodländer that a weak electrolyte usually becomes a strong electrolyte when its weak ion is converted into a complex ion."

Chapter IX.

Internal Pressure.[1]

DEFINITIONS.

In Chapter VII it was shown that the internal pressure or cohesion of liquids is of fundamental importance in determining whether their solutions will obey Raoult's law. It is accordingly desirable to examine the methods whereby internal pressures may be computed and to give actual values to serve as a basis for solubility predictions. A great deal has been written upon the subject, as can be seen from the length of the bibliography—by no means complete—given in this chapter. Upon reading this, however, one is struck not only by the wide divergence in the values for internal pressure calculated by different methods, but also by the absence of any very clear definition of internal pressure. No one can doubt the existence of a cohesion in liquids which prevents them from undergoing any large increase in volume, even when very large negative pressures are applied. In fact, negative pressures of 72 atmospheres have been found by Meyer[2] in the case of ether before the liquid ruptured, and there is reason to believe that if the accidental formation of vapor could be prevented far greater negative pressures could be supported by the liquid. One might, therefore, define internal pressure as the maximum negative pressure that a liquid could support if no nuclei of vapor were allowed to form. The theory of van der Waals of the continuity of the liquid and vapor states postulates the possibility of going from liquid to vapor not only by the usual discontinuous path $abdfg$, Fig. 1, but by the continuous path $abcdefg$. Of course, the latter path could be realized only if the molecules all remained equidistant from each other at every point on this path between b and c, and this is manifestly impossible on account of thermal agitation, so that although it is possible to expand a liquid below b, there will always be a sudden break back to the straight line bdf long before the point c is reached.

It would, however, be possible to calculate the negative pressure at c if the equation for the curve were known, and it might safely be assumed that an equation which gave both of the experimentally realizable portions ab and fg would also give the hypothetical portion bc,

---

[1] See review by W. C. McC. Lewis, *Trans. Faraday Soc.*, 7, 94 (1911).
[2] Meyer, "Zur Kenntniss des negativen Druckes in Flüssigkeiten," Abh. d. Deut. Bunsen-Ges., No. 6 (1911), Knapp, Halle.

the value of the negative pressure at c being obtained by the aid of the relation $dP/dV = 0$ at this point.

The practical difficulty attending this definition is the lack of an equation of state which successfully accounts for the behavior of both liquid and vapor. The determination of what might be called the maximum tensile strength of a liquid is therefore both practically and theoretically unfeasible.

The conception underlying several of the discussions of internal pressure is that of a cohesive force actually existing in a liquid. Now

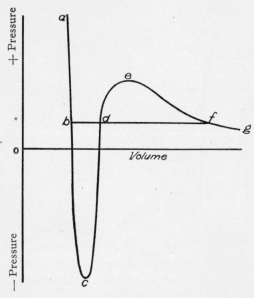

Fig. 1.—Negative Pressure in the Light of the van der Waals Equation.

it should be obvious that a state of equilibrium exists in a liquid between attractive and repulsive forces and external pressure, so that no calculation of attractive forces can be made unless they can be differentiated from the repulsive forces which the low compressibility of liquids indicates are extremely great. Our present conception that intermolecular forces are due solely to the electron structure of the molecule makes it far more difficult to separate the attractive from the repulsive forces than it used to be in former days when molecules were mostly thought of as rigid spheres subject to attractive forces operating with undiminished magnitude to hold the molecules together even when in "contact" or "collision." The two forces were evidently conceived as different in kind, just as the force holding two magnets in contact is different from the repulsive force which opposes it. One is magnetic, the other is due to the slight compression of their masses.

If we can measure the increasing attraction as the two magnets approach each other we feel confident that we can calculate the force holding them in contact. This conception is illustrated by Fig. 2, where the attractive force is supposed to be entirely distinct from the repulsive force, and even though they are in equilibrium at the point of intersection they have a real magnitude which can be determined from their respective curves.

Our present conception, however, is that as the molecules approach each other the attraction, at first increasing, passes a maximum and then decreases, as shown in Fig. 3, changing sign finally to a repulsion, the molecules being in equilibrium when the repulsion just equals the

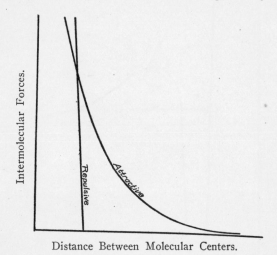

Distance Between Molecular Centers.

FIG. 2.—Older Conception of Attractive and Repulsive Forces.

external pressure. Such a curve might, it is true, be represented by an equation containing different kinds of terms, but the assumption that this would indicate two forces would be highly artificial.

The equation of van der Waals is based upon this conception of hard incompressible molecules of volume b, attracted by a force a/v^2, which is aided by the external pressure in balancing a repulsive force, $RT/(v-b)$ due to the thermal agitation and the rebound of these hard molecules upon collision. It has long been recognized that the simple van der Waals equation cannot adequately represent the facts, and that the actual molecular volumes are not constant as implied by the constant b. Probably the most direct evidence upon this point is furnished by the compressibility, which does not approach zero at absolute zero, as it would if the molecules were inelastic spheres in contact.[3] The variability of b with pressure is also indicated by other

[3] Grüneisen, *Ann. Physik.*, 33, 1239 (1910).

observations.[4] When, therefore, one attempts to say what would be the attractive forces operating in a liquid in which the repulsive forces were by some sort of magic annihilated, there should be no surprise if the results are somewhat vague.

FROM EQUATIONS OF STATE.

It seems evident that our estimate of the internal forces operating in liquids can best be drawn from an equation of state provided that it accurately represents the behavior of the liquid. As was pointed

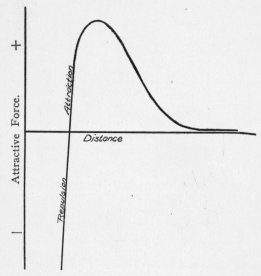

FIG. 3.—Newer Conception of Intermolecular Forces.

out in Chapter VII, p. 70, it seems very reasonable to expect that two liquids have like internal forces, and may therefore be expected to obey Raoult's law, provided their equations of state are identical. The only equation of state whose validity is not open to question is the thermodynamic equation

$$P + \left(\frac{\partial E}{\partial V}\right)_T = T \left(\frac{\partial P}{\partial T}\right)_V. \tag{1}$$

It is possible to remove the ambiguity usually attending the idea of internal pressure by defining it as $T(\partial P/\partial T)_V$,[5] the right hand member of the above equation, whose value, as previously pointed out

[4] Cf. Richards, *J. Am. Chem. Soc.*, **36**, 617 (1914).
[5] Hildebrand, *J. Am. Chem. Soc.*, **43**, 500 (1921).

(Equation VII-6), is easily obtainable either by direct measurement or from the coefficients of expansion and compressibility, since

$$T\left(\frac{\partial P}{\partial T}\right)_V = -T\frac{\alpha}{\beta}.$$

The right hand member of this equation was proposed by Dupré[6] as a measure of internal pressure.

Table I gives values of the internal pressure so calculated for some liquids of low polarity.

TABLE I.

INTERNAL PRESSURES IN MEGABARS AT 20°.

	$\alpha \cdot 10^6$.	$\beta \cdot 10^7$.	$293\alpha/\beta$.
iso-Hexane	1445	1450	2920
Octane	1181	1167	2970
Ethyl benzene	961	807	3490
m-Xylene	994	789	3690
Carbon tetrachloride	1229	978	3690
Toluene	1099	842	3830
Chloroform	1276	963	3880
Benzene	1242	888	4100
Ethylene bromide	967	596	4760
Bromine	1111	602	5400
Bromoform	939[7]	486	5660
Mercury	181	40	13200

The values of α have been taken from various sources.[8] Since the data upon compressibility published by different observers are not always very concordant, and since relative rather than absolute values are here desired, the table uses only data from a single reliable source, viz., from Richards[9] and co-workers. These observers, in common with most others, do not give compressibility as a differential, but, instead, the mean compressibility over a large range. Since the compressibility varies considerably with the pressure it has been necessary for our purpose to extrapolate their data to atmospheric pressure, at which the values of expansion have been measured. The pressure unit is the megabar.[10]

The familiar equation of state of van der Waals, in spite of its inaccuracy, may serve as a useful criterion for *relative* values of internal pressure, because the relatively large number of values of the van der Waals "constants" *a* and *b* which are to be found in the literature make it particularly available for the purpose, since either

[6] Dupré, *Ann. Chim. phys.*, **2**, 201 (1864).
[7] This value was obtained with bromoform which was evidently impure, since its freezing point was 2.5° instead of 7.8°.
[8] Thorpe, *J. Chem. Soc.*, **37**, 141 (1880); **63**, 273 (1893); Louguinine, *Ann. Chim. phys.* [4], **11**, 453 (1867); Pierre, *ibid.* [3], **20**, 1 (1847); **21**, 336 (1847); **33**, 199 (1851); Pinette, *Ann.*, **243**, 32 (1888); Weger, *ibid.*, **221**, 67 (1883).
[9] Richards, Stull, Mathews and Speyers, *J. Am. Chem. Soc.*, **34**, 971 (1912); Richards and Shipley, *ibid.*, **38**, 989 (1916).
[10] 1 megabar = 0.987 atmosphere per sq. cm., = 10^6 dynes per sq. cm.

of the terms a/v^2 or $RT/(v-b)$ may serve as rough measures of internal pressure. The values of a and b available have been calculated chiefly from the critical data.

Inasmuch as critical data are not available for very many substances, it is gratifying to note that van Laar has contributed a method for the calculation of a on an additive basis.[11] He has shown that $\sqrt{a}$ for a molecule is the sum of the values of $\sqrt{a}$ for the atoms composing it. He gives the following values for $\sqrt{a}.10^4$:

H	1.6	P	6.4	Kr	6.9
C	3.1 ; 1.55 ; 0	S	6.3	Sb	8.9
N	2.9	Cl	5.4	I	8.8
O	2.7	A	5.2	Xe	9.1
F	2.9	Se	7.1	Hg	11.0
Ne	2.0	Br	6.9		

There is a constitutive influence apparent, especially with carbon compounds, where the surrounding atoms may exert a partial or even complete screening effect. Thus in compounds like CCl_4, C_6H_{14}, and C_2H_5Cl, the value of $\sqrt{a}$ for carbon is 0. In doubly bound carbon, such as in C_6H_6 the value of $\sqrt{a}.10^4$ is 1.55. It reaches its full value of 3.1 in C_2H_2, CO, etc.

The following examples are reproduced from van Laar's paper:

$$a.10^4$$

Cl_2	$(2 \times 5.4)^2$	$= 108$
CS_2	$(3.1 + 2 \times 6.3)^2$	$= 246$
C_6H_{14}	$(0 + 14 \times 1.6)^2$	$= 502$
C_6H_6	$(6 \times 1.55 + 6 \times 1.6)^2$	$= 357$
C_2H_5Cl	$(0 + 5 \times 1.6 + 5.4)^2$	$= 180$
C_4H_4S	$(4 \times 1.55 + 4 \times 1.6 + 6.3)^2$	$= 357$

It is thus possible to calculate values of a with sufficient accuracy for our present purpose of calculating relative internal pressures even where critical data are lacking.

Table 2 gives values of a/v^2 for a number of liquids. Data for a have, in general, been taken from the Landolt u. Börnstein Tabellen or calculated by the method of van Laar, the values obtained in the latter way being denoted by an asterisk. v is obtained from the molal weight and the density of the liquid at 20°.

Other data may be used for obtaining a and b, such as those for coefficient of expansion. Differentiating the equation with respect to v at constant pressure gives

$$-\frac{2a}{v}(v-b) + \frac{a}{v^2} = R\left(\frac{\partial T}{\partial V}\right)_P = -\frac{2a}{v^3} \cdot \frac{RT}{P + a/v^2} + \frac{a}{v^2}.$$

[11] Van Laar, *J. chim. phys.*, **14**, 3 (1916).

Neglecting P in comparison with a/v^2 and putting $(\partial V/\partial T)_P = v\alpha$ where α is the coefficient of expansion, we have [12]

$$\frac{a}{v^2} = \frac{R}{V}\left(\frac{1}{\alpha} + 2T\right). \qquad (2)$$

Table 3 gives values of $(1/\alpha + 2T)/v$.

A similar expression could be obtained for calculating a/v^2 from the compressibility [13] but this would be of little use. Further applications of the van der Waals' equation might be described, but its well-known inaccuracy makes it seem inadvisable to give more than a few references.[14]

TABLE 2.

RELATIVE INTERNAL PRESSURES FROM VAN DER WAALS' EQUATION.

Liquid	$a.10^4$	v_{20_0}	$\frac{a}{v^2}.10^8$
Nickel carbonyl	548 *	135	246
Octane	728	177	232
Decane	968	196.5	252
Hexane	493	130.5	290
Ethyl ether	346	103.8	320
Mesitylene	684	139.0	356
Stannic chloride	536	117.0	390
Ethyl benzene	570	121.0	390
m-Xylene	605	123.0	400
Carbon tetrachloride	389	96.6	416
Toluene	480	106.5	428
Ethyl iodide	283 *	80.7	435
Fluorobenzene	397	93.8	452
Chloroform	293	80.4	454
Chlorine	118	50.2	460
Benzene	373	88.8	472
Chlorobenzene	507	101.8	488
Naphthalene	792	123 [15]	516
Bromobenzene	569	105.0	516
Iodobenzene	659	112.2	524
Ethylene chloride	337	78.8	544
Ethylene bromide	408 * (279)	85.2	550 (390)
Thiophene	357 * (413)	79.0	572 (662)
Phenanthrene	1410 *	158 [16]	570
p-Dibromobenzene	860 *	120	600
Carbon bisulfide	220	60.2	610
Bromoform	497 *	86.6	660
Bromine	191 *	51.3	730
Sulfur monochloride	548 *	80.5	850
Iodine	310 *	60 [17]	860
Phosphorus	659	69.5 [18]	1370

[12] Cf. Benedicks, *Z. anorg. chem.*, **47**, 455 (1905).
[13] Cf. Winther, *Z. physik. Chem.*, **60**, 603 (1907).
[14] Traube, *Z. physik. Chem.*, **68**, 291 (1909); W. C. McC. Lewis, *Phil. Mag.* [6], **28**, 104 (1912); Davies, *ibid.* [6], **24**, 415 (1912).
[15] Extrapolated from data by Lossen and Zander, *Ann.*, **225**, 111 (1884).
[16] Extrapolated from data by Schiff, *ibid.*, **223**, 247 (1884).
[17] Extrapolated from data by Billet, *Mém. Inst. France*, **1855**, 292.
[18] Abegg-Auerbach, "Handbuch d. anorg. Chem.," **5**, p. 373.
* Calculated by the method of van Laar, loc. cit.

TABLE 3.

RELATIVE INTERNAL PRESSURES FROM COEFFICIENT OF EXPANSION.

Liquid	$\alpha.10^4$	v	$\dfrac{1}{\alpha} + 2 \times 293$
			v
Octane	118	177.0	0.81
Silicon tetrachloride	144	114.5	1.12
Ether	165	103.8	1.15
Stannic chloride	118	117.0	1.22
m-Xylene	99	123.0	1.30
Ethyl benzene	96	121.0	1.34
Toluene	110	106.5	1.41
Carbon tetrachloride	124	96.6	1.44
Benzene	124	89.8	1.56
Phosphorus trichloride	118	87.1	1.67
Chloroform	127	80.4	1.71
Ethyl iodide	118	80.7	1.77
Ethylene chloride	116	78.8	1.83
Sulfur monochloride	97	80.5	2.10
Carbon bisulfide	122	60.2	2.27
Bromine	111	51.3	2.89

Sutherland [19] has given an equation of state containing more constants, and therefore a greater flexibility to enable it to fit the facts:

$$P + \frac{\text{M}^2 l}{2v^2} = \frac{R'T}{v}\left(1 + \frac{\sqrt{T}}{B} \cdot \frac{A-v}{v-C}\right), \qquad (3)$$

where M is the molecular weight, and l, R', A, B and C are constants. In this equation the term $\text{M}^2 l/2v^2$ has the dimensions of pressure, and like a/v^2 in the van der Waals equation, may be considered as a measure of the resemblance of two liquids. Sutherland has calculated the values of l for a number of liquids by five distinct methods, from the expansion and compressibility of gases and of liquids, from the latent heat of vaporization, from the critical temperature and pressure, and from the surface tension. These different methods yield values of l which agree reasonably well. Table 4 gives $\text{M}^2 l/v^2$ for a number of liquids of low polarity, the figures denoting relative values only, since we are not here particularly concerned with the absolute values or with the units used.

It will be noted that the order of arrangement of the liquids is essentially the same in Tables 1 to 4, and it is safe to say that other equations of state of the same general form would yield this same order.

FROM HEAT OF VAPORIZATION.

We have seen that the term $(\partial E/\partial V)_T$ in the thermodynamic equation of state (VII, 1) may serve to measure internal pressure.

[19] Sutherland, *Phil. Mag.* [5], **35**, 211 (1893).

TABLE 4.
RELATIVE INTERNAL PRESSURES—SUTHERLAND.

Hexane	350	Benzene	556
Silicon tetrachloride	363	Chloroform	572
Ethyl ether	406	Phosphorus trichloride	573
Stannic chloride	448	Bromobenzene	607
Xylene	460	Iodobenzene	740
Ethyl benzene	482	Ethylene bromide	710
Carbon tetrachloride	490	Carbon bisulfide	743
Toluene	497		

If this quantity is assumed to be proportional inversely to some power of the volume we may write [20]

$$\left(\frac{\partial E}{\partial V}\right)_T = \frac{a}{v^n}. \tag{4}$$

Now, if the liquid could be expanded isothermally until it attains the volume of the saturated vapor, v_v, the energy absorbed would be the same as that absorbed in ordinary vaporization, L_v, hence

$$L_v = \int_v^{v_v} \frac{a}{v^n} dv = \frac{a}{1-n}\left(\frac{1}{v_v^{n-1}} - \frac{1}{v^{n-1}}\right). \tag{5}$$

If n is not much less than 2 the term containing v_v can be neglected, giving

$$L_v = \frac{a}{(n-1)v^{n-1}}, \tag{6}$$

and [21]

$$\frac{a}{v^n} = \frac{(n-1)L}{v} = \left(\frac{\partial E}{\partial V}\right)_T. \tag{7}$$

The ratio L_v/v should therefore, serve to give relative internal pressures, as suggested by Dupré [22] and later by Stefan [23] with whose name it is usually associated. Stefan considered that the work of carrying a molecule from the interior of a liquid into the surface is half of the energy absorbed in vaporization. Harkins and Roberts [24] have considered this critically, and say "it seems evident that what is meant by Stefan is not the 'work' or free energy, but rather the mean total energy required to carry the molecule from the interior of the liquid into the surface," and they have shown this to be far from true.

It has been customary to calculate this "work" from the product

[20] In the van der Waals equation n = 2. The following discussion would remain valid if we should use the more general expression $a/(v-C)^n$.

[21] Cf. Hildebrand, *J. Am. Chem. Soc.*, **43**, 500 (1921).

[22] Dupré, *Ann. chim. phys.*, **6**, 283 (1865).

[23] Stefan, *Wied. Ann.*, **29**, 655 (1886).

[24] Harkins and Roberts, *J. Am. Chem. Soc.*, **44**, 653 (1922).

of the internal pressure with the molal volume of the liquid, and equate it to $\frac{1}{2}L_v$. The resulting expression has been used recently by Walden[25] and by Herz[26] for calculating internal pressures, the former combining it with an empirical relationship, $L/v = 3.64\ \gamma_b$, where γ_b is the surface tension at the boiling point.

The revised form of Trouton's rule[27] discovered by the author and referred to in the preceding chapter, p. 93, makes it possible to calculate the entire vapor pressure curve of a normal liquid, and hence the heat of vaporization, from a single point, such as the boiling point. This relation may be used to substitute the more accessible boiling point for the heat of vaporization in making the calculation of L_v/v. By plotting $\log p$ against $\log T$ for the vapor pressure of one normal liquid a curve is obtained which may be superimposed upon the similar curve for any other normal liquid by sliding it along any line whose equation is $\log p = \log T +$ const. Consequently, when but a single point on the vapor pressure curve of one substance is known, such as the boiling point, the entire curve may be constructed by the above means. Furthermore, the tangent to this curve at any point has a slope equal to L/RT. From this the value of L at any temperature can be obtained. Subtracting RT^{pv} gives the value of the heat of vaporization at constant volume, L_v. This was determined for a number of liquids having different boiling points, and it was found that the relation between $L - RT$ at 20° and the boiling point of the liquid could be expressed by the following equation:

$$L - \overset{pv}{RT} = 5200 + 30t_b,$$

where t_b represents the boiling point.

Table 5 gives relative values of internal pressure so calculated from the boiling points.

From Surface Tension.

The surface tension may serve as a very convenient basis for estimating the internal forces operating in a liquid. When a surface is extended 1 sq. cm. the work done is that necessary to bring a new layer of molecules into the surface, and we may imagine the same work being done by a direct pull of the molecules upwards from the interior into the surface. Since the range of molecular attraction is undoubtedly very minute, and of the order of magnitude of the mean distance between the molecules, r, the force required for the direct upward pull of the molecules would have to' be very large, since the distance through which it operates is so very small, in order that the work may have the same moderate values as γ ergs. The direct force required to hold the molecules in the surface is therefore of the order of magnitude of γ/r.

[25] Walden, Z. physik. Chem., 66, 385 (1909).
[26] Herz, Z. Elektrochem., 20, 332 (1914).
[27] Hildebrand, J. Am. Chem. Soc., 37, 970 (1915); 40, 45 (1918).

TABLE 5.

RELATIVE INTERNAL PRESSURES FROM BOILING POINTS.

Liquid	t_b	v	$\dfrac{5200 + 30t_b}{v}$
Nickel carbonyl	43.2	135	48.0
Octane	125	177	50.5
Decane	173	196.5	52.8
Hexane	69	130.5	55.6
Ethyl ether	34.6	103.8	60.1
Silicon tetrachloride	59.6	114.5	61.0
Mesitylene	165	139.0	73.0
Stannic chloride	113	117.0	73.5
m-Xylene	139	123.0	76.2
Ethyl benzene	136	121.0	76.7
Carbon tetrachloride	76.5	96.6	77.5
Toluene	110.7	106.5	80.0
Fluorobenzene	85	93.8	82.0
Chlorine	33.6	50.2	84.0
Benzene	80	88.8	85.6
Phosphorus trichloride	76	87.1	86.0
Chloroform	61	80.4	87.5
Chlorobenzene	132	101.8	90.2
Ethyl iodide	72	80.7	91.3
Bromobenzene	156	105.0	94.1
Naphthalene	218	123 [28]	95.5
Iodobenzene	188.5	112.2	96.8
Ethylene chloride	83.7	78.8	97.8
Thiophene	84	79.0	97.7
Phenanthrene	340	158 [29]	98.0
p-Dibromobenzene	219	120	98
Ethylene bromide	129	85.2	106
Phosphorus tribromide	172	95.5	108
Carbon disulfide	46	60.2	109
Bromoform	151	86.6	112
Sulfur monochloride	138	80.5	116
Bromine	59	51.3	136
Iodine	184	60 [30]	180
Phosphorus	287	69.5 [31]	199

The same relation may be brought out by imagining a column of liquid having 1 sq. cm. cross section which is ruptured in either of two ways, first by starting the rupture at one point from a minute bubble whose surface is then extended to 2 sq. cm. against the force of surface tension, requiring 2γ ergs of work; and second, by pulling the liquid apart against the force of cohesion, which of course varies with the distance, but which extends only through a very short range, so that the ends of the ruptured column are removed from practically all attraction when but a very minute distance apart.

These ideas were early discussed by Thomas Young [32] and by

[28] Extrapolated from data by Lossen and Zander, *Ann.*, **225**, 111 (1884).
[29] Extrapolated from data by Schiff, *ibid.*, **223**, 247 (1884).
[30] Extrapolated from data by Billet, *Mém. Inst. France*, **1855**, 292.
[31] Abegg-Auerbach, Handbuch d. anorg. Chem., **5**, p. 373.
[32] Thomas Young, *Phil. Trans. Roy. Soc., London*, **1**, 65 (1805). See also collected works.

Laplace [33] and led, at the hands of the latter, to the following related equations for the force acting parallel to the surface, the surface tension, and the force K, normal to the surface:

$$\gamma = \pi\,\rho^2 \int_0^\infty x\,\psi\,(x)\,dx, \qquad (8)$$

$$K = 2\pi\,\rho^2 \int_0^\infty \psi\,(x)\,dx. \qquad (9)$$

In these equations x represents distance and $\psi(x)$ is the function which states how the attractive force varies with the distance; ρ is the density.[34] To get an approximate idea of the relation between K and γ we may integrate these equations assuming that molecular attraction varies inversely as some power of the distance. Sutherland [35] has assumed an inverse fourth power, and justified it by extensive calculations. Kleemann [36] and Jarvinen [37] have decided in favor of an inverse fifth power. Considerations set forth at the beginning of this Chapter render it doubtful whether any inverse power law can be strictly accurate, but if the area under the curves in Figs. 2 and 3 are substantially the same the assumptions involved in Fig. 2 may give results not far from the truth. We may, therefore, assume as an approximation that $\psi(x) = k/x^q$ where k is a constant. Equations 8 and 9 then become, respectively,

$$\gamma = \pi\,\rho^2 k \int \frac{dx}{x^{q-1}}, \qquad (10)$$

and
$$K = 2\pi\,\rho^2 k \int \frac{dx}{x^q}. \qquad (11)$$

These equations may be integrated between the limits $x = r$ and $x = \infty$, since these are the values at which the attraction becomes zero. This process gives

$$\gamma = \frac{\pi\,\rho^2 k}{(q-2)r^{q-2}}, \qquad (12)$$

$$K = \frac{2\pi\,\rho^2 k}{(q-1)r^{q-1}}, \qquad (13)$$

and finally,

$$K = \frac{2q-4}{q-1} \cdot \frac{\gamma}{r}. \qquad (14)$$

[33] Laplace, Oeuvres, Vol. IV, 389..

[34] For the derivation of these equations cf. Rayleigh, *Phil. Mag.* [5], 30, 285, 456 (1890).

[35] Sutherland, *Phil. Mag.* [5], 22, 81 (1886); 27, 305 (1889); 35, 211 (1893); 39, 1 (1895), and others.

[36] Kleemann, *Phil. Mag.*, 19, 783 (1910).

[37] Jarvinen, *Z. physik. Chem.*, 82, 541 (1913); 88, 428 (1914).

TABLE 6.

RELATIVE INTERNAL PRESSURES FROM SURFACE TENSION AND TOTAL SURFACE ENERGY.

	$\gamma(20°)$	E_σ	$\gamma/v^{1/3}$	$E_\sigma/v^{1/3}$
Nickel carbonyl	14.59	46.8	2.84	9.1
Hexane	19.25	49.5	3.80	9.8
Octane	21.52	48.4	3.83	8.6
Silicon tetrachloride	16.65	47.4	3.42	9.7
Ethyl ether	17.1	47.8	3.64	10.2
Stannic chloride	26.62	....	5.44	....
Mesitylene	28.32	57	5.46	11.0
m-Xylene	28.07	64	5.64	12.8
Carbon tetrachloride	26.56	63	5.78	14.3
Ethyl benzene	28.94	61	5.86	12.3
Toluene	28.63	63	6.06	13.3
Phosphorus trichloride	29.10	68	6.07	14.2
Fluorobenzene	27.96	46	6.18	10.1
Chloroform	26.76	63	6.20	14.6
Benzene	28.90	69	6.48	15.5
Ethyl iodide	29.1	65	6.74	15.0
Chlorobenzene	32.9	68	7.05	14.6
Bromobenzene	35	72	7.5	15.4
Thiophene	32	74	7.5	17.3
Ethylene chloride	32.1	73	7.5	17.0
Iodobenzene	37.4	67	7.8	14.0
p-Dibromobenzene	39.0	66	7.9	13.4
Ethylene bromide	38.4	76	8.7	17.2
Carbon bisulfide	34.5	75	8.7	18.9
Sulfur monochloride	43.0	84	10.0	19.5
Bromine	39	196	10.5	53
Phosphorus	51.1	..	12.4	....

Since the molal volume, v, is proportional to r^3, we may write

$$K = k'\frac{\gamma}{v^{1/3}} \qquad (15)$$

where k' is presumably a universal constant.

Table 6 gives values of $\gamma/v^{1/3}$ for most of the liquids treated in the preceding tables, and shows the same general order of arrangement. The data are taken for the most part from the extensive summary by Harkins, Davies and Clark.[38]

Mathews[39] has calculated values for the van der Waals "constant" a from the assumption that $K = 3\,\gamma/r$. He uses a number of ingenious methods for attaining his aim which cannot be reproduced here, but by dividing his values of a by v^2 the figures shown in Table 7 are obtained which give an arrangement in excellent accord with those in previous tables.

There are other considerations which indicate that not the surface tension, or the free energy of surface formation, but rather the total energy of surface formation, E_σ, should be used as our basis of com-

[38] Harkins, Davies and Clark, *J. Am. Chem. Soc.*, **39**, 555 (1917).
[39] A. P. Mathews, *J. phys. Chem.*, **17**, 603 (1913).

TABLE 7.
INTERNAL PRESSURES—MATHEWS.

Octane	1670	Toluene	2650
Hexane	1700	Carbon tetrachloride	2660
Ethyl ether	1970	Chloroform	2910
Xylene	2400	Benzene	2940
Ethyl acetate	2460	Ethylene bromide	3900
Stannic chloride	2500	Carbon bisulfide	3950

parison. E_σ can be calculated from γ and $d\gamma/dT$ by the Thomson equation

$$E_\sigma = \gamma - T \frac{d\gamma}{dT}. \tag{16}$$

If we maintain the terms in the thermodynamic equation of state, $T(\partial P/\partial T)_V$ and $(\partial E/\partial V)_T$ as the basis for defining internal pressure it is obvious that the latter term, which is the total energy absorbed in the expansion of the liquid, is related to the total energy, not the free energy, absorbed in the formation of new surface. Moreover it is possible to show the direct connection between L/v previously used and $E_\sigma/v^{1/3}$ as follows:[40] Let us take 1 mol of liquid, having a volume, v, and break it up into n drops of equal radius, r. The volume of these drops will be $v = 4\pi r^3 n/3$, and the surface, $\sigma = 4\pi r^2 n$. Eliminating r we have $\sigma = 4.84 v^{2/3} n^{1/3}$. The energy absorbed in forming n drops from one would be $\sigma E_\sigma = 4.84 v^{2/3} E_\sigma (n^{1/3} - 1)$. If the surface tension remained constant down to "drops" each containing but a single molecule, when n becomes 6.06×10^{23}, the energy absorbed would equal the internal heat of vaporization, and we would have $L_v = 40.9 v^{2/3} E_\sigma$ joules. If, as is probably the case, the surface tension remains constant at least to drops containing 13 molecules, where, with hexagonal packing, one molecule would be completely shielded by those on the surface, we can calculate a lower limit for the value of L_v, obtaining $17.4 v^{2/3} E_\sigma$. As a matter of fact, the heat of vaporization lies between the limits given and corresponds approximately to the expression $L_v = 25 v^{2/3} E_\sigma$. We see, therefore, that $E_\sigma/v^{1/3}$ is proportional to L_v/v, and hence, by the earlier discussion, proportional also to internal pressure.

Table 6 includes values of E_σ taken from the extensive tables of Harkins, Davies and Clark.[41] The figures for $d\gamma/dT$ obtained by different observers are often very discordant, so that the calculated values for E_σ are often widely different. The values for $E_\sigma/v^{1/3}$ given in the last column are very inaccurate, and are given only to show that they confirm the previous order as well as could be expected. The general agreement in the order of arrangement given by $\gamma/v^{1/3}$ and $E_\sigma/v^{1/3}$ justifies the use of the former expression for practical purposes in place of the often unknown and usually inaccurate data for $E_\sigma/v^{1/3}$.

[40] Hildebrand, *J. Am. Chem. Soc.*, **43**, 500 (1921).
[41] Harkins, Davies and Clark, *J. Am. Chem. Soc.*, **39**, 555 (1917).

Harkins [42] has discussed this matter from a theoretical standpoint, showing that E_σ is more closely connected with internal pressure or cohesion.

While surface tension and total surface energy furnish abundant data very useful in the application of the theory of solubility to particular cases, there are, however, two considerations which affect the reliance which may be placed upon such criteria. One is the fact that the surface tension and the total surface energy measure not the condition in the liquid only, but the difference between the attractive forces in the liquid and in the vapor. Both γ and E_σ become 0 at the critical temperature while $T(\partial P/\partial T)_V$ is still large.

The other consideration is that a polar grouping in part of a molecule, though greatly affecting the internal pressure, may not be apparent in the surface tension, as Langmuir and Harkins [43] have shown, because the orientation of the molecules in the surface is such as to leave the non-polar portion in the surface.

From Solubility Data.

It is possible to arrange a series of liquids on the basis of solubility data alone, without reference to any of the previous methods of determining internal pressure, and in many respects this is the most satisfactory basis of all. A solute of high internal pressure should show decreasing solubilities in a series of solvents of progressively decreasing internal pressure. Conversely, a solute of low internal pressure should become less and less soluble as solvents of higher internal pressure are chosen. A substance in the middle of the series should be most soluble in its near neighbors, with decreasing solubilities towards both ends of the series. The establishment of the series is at the outset complicated by the fact that solubilities less than the ideal do not indicate which of the components has the higher internal pressure. This, together with the irrational method usually employed to express solubilities and the failure to exclude polar substances, doubtless prevented the earlier recognition of the solubility series.

The evidence for the series from solubility data themselves is most striking when solutes belonging at the extremes are employed. Several sets of data satisfying this condition are given in Table 8 and show no important deviations from the order obtained for the previous tables. A large amount of further confirmatory material is contained in the later chapters.

The graphic representation of solubility data by the plot of log N against $1/T$, as discussed in Chapter IV, page 38, and Chapter V, p. 58, may serve to illustrate the solubility series. Thus the data for the solubilities of iodine and sulfur, Chap. XIV, Figs. 1 and 2, both substances of high internal pressure, give a family of curves converg-

[42] Harkins, *Proc. Nat. Acad. Sci.*, 5, 566 (1919).

[43] Langmuir, *Met. Chem. Eng.*, 15, 469 (1916); Harkins, Brown, Davies and Clark, *J. Am. Chem. Soc.*, 39, 354-64, 541-96 (1917).

TABLE 8.

INTERNAL PRESSURES FROM RELATIVE SOLUBILITIES. MOL PERCENT.

	H_2[44] 20°	N_2[44] 20°	CO[44] 20°	CH_4[45] 25°	$C_6H_4Br_2$[46] 25°	Phenanthrene[46] 25°	I_2[47] 25°	S_8[48] 25°	Anthracene[46] 25°
Hexane	....	....	....	0.31	8.6	4.2	....	0.14	0.18
Heptane	.·...	....	....	....	18.3	15.1	0.68	0.14	....
Ethyl ether	0.040	0.061	0.089	0.26	....	....	....	0.83	0.59
Xylene	....	....	....	....	19.3	18.6	1.10	0.50	0.63
Carbon tetrachloride	0.037	0.053	0.077	0.21	....	....	....	0.74	....
Toluene	....	0.043	0.063	....	....	....	2.28	0.56	0.81
Chloroform	....	0.041	0.061	....	....	....	....	0.64	....
Benzene	0.026	....	....	0.18	21.7	20.7	(Solvate)	....	....
Ethylene bromide	....	....	....	....	....	....	....	2.0	....
Carbon bisulfide	....	0.013	0.020	....	22.4	....	5.70	13.8	1.12

[44] Just, Z. physik. Chem., **37**, 342 (1901).
[45] MacDaniel, J. phys. Chem., **15**, 587 (1911).
[46] Hildebrand, J. Am. Chem. Soc., **39**, 2293 (1917).
[47] Hildebrand and Jenks, **42**, 2180 (1920).
[48] Ibid., **43**, 2172 (1921).

ing to the melting point, except for the lower curves for sulfur where two liquid phases result when the sulfur melts, so that N_2 does not become unity till much higher temperatures are reached. The solubility becomes progressively less as the positive deviation from Raoult's law increases from top to bottom of the plot. The spacing of these curves at any temperature might be used to deduce a solubility series. Since log p^s/p° — log N may be used to express deviations from Raoult's law,[49] and since p^s/p° equals the ideal solubility, N_i, the difference log N_i — log N may be used to express deviations from Raoult's law and hence the solubility series when the position of the solute therein is known.

Or, instead of the above difference one may use the slope of the curve, since this increases, in general, as the positive deviation from Raoult's law increases. This has been done by Mortimer,[51] who expresses the non-ideality of the solution as the ratio of the actual slope to the ideal slope. This is related to, though not equal to, the difference between the heat of solution and the heat of fusion.[52] The ideal slope is, of course, equal to the molal heat of fusion divided by 4.58.[53]

The difference in slope for the various solubility curves may be expressed by introducing a factor, f, into Equation IV-7, giving

$$\log N = \frac{-fL_f}{4.58}\left(\frac{1}{T} - \frac{1}{T_m}\right). \tag{17}$$

The factor, f, may be calculated from differences in internal pressure of the two components of the solution. Mortimer gives a table of relative internal pressures, Table 9, derived from solubility data, and which may, in turn, be used for the calculation of solubilities. He has found it possible to include a number of highly polar substances in this table and to calculate their solubility relations fairly well in a large number of cases.

It will be noted that the agreement with previous tables is fairly good. The factors, f, in Equation 17 are connected with the values in Table 9 in the following way:

When both solvent and solute have internal pressures greater than that of naphthalene

f = $K_1 - K_2 + 1$, where K_1 is the larger value, and K_2 the smaller, taken from Table 9.

When K_1 and K_2 are both less than unity, and $K_2 > K_1$,

$$f = \frac{1}{K_1} - \frac{1}{K_2} + 1.$$

When $K_1 > 1$ and $K_2 < 1$,

$$f = K_1 + \frac{1}{K_2} - 1.$$

[49] Cf. Chapter V, p. 3 ff.
[51] Mortimer, *J. Am. Chem. Soc.*, **44**, 1416 (1922); **45**, 633 (1923).
[52] Chapter VI, p. 3 ff.
[53] Chapter IV, p. 13.

TABLE 9.

RELATIVE INTERNAL PRESSURES, REFERRED TO NAPHTHALENE, AS CALCULATED
FROM SOLUBILITY DATA.

Substance	Relative Int. Pres.	Substance	Relative Int. Pres.
Hexane	0.56	Carbazole	1.12
Ethyl ether	0.66	Carbon disulfide	1.13
Acetic anhydride	0.76	Trinitrophenol	1.14
Paraldehyde	0.77	Dinitrophenol	1.15
Menthol	0.78	p-Nitrophenol	1.17
Ethyl acetate	0.83	Benzanthrone	1.20
Carbon tetrachloride	0.84	Anthraquinone	1.22
Phthalic anhydride	0.91	Antimony trichloride	1.23
Bromotoluene	0.93	Antimony tribromide	1.25
Bromobenzene	0.94	Thymol	1.26
Benzene	0.94	Benzophenone	1.27
Toluene	0.93	Acetophenone	1.30
Ethylene dibromide	0.95	Benzil	1.30
p-Dichlorobenzene	0.95	Aluminum bromide	1.30
p-Dibromobenzene	0.95	Acetone	1.32
Chloroform	0.95	Naphthylamines	1.33
Chlorotoluene	0.97	Toluidines	1.35
Chlorobenzene	0.98	Benzoic acid	1.38
Acenaphthene	0.98	Naphthols	1.40
Naphthalene	1.00	Trichloro-acetic acid	1.42
Diphenylamine	1.00	Aniline	1.46
Phenanthrene	1.02	Nitro-anilines	1.65
Fluorene	1.04	Sulfur	1.70
Anthracene	1.05	Iodine	1.85
Diphenyl methane	1.06	p-Azoxy-anisole	1.87
Triphenyl methane	1.07	Acetic acid	1.95
Nitrobenzene	1.07	Acetanilide	2.78
Nitronaphthalene	1.08	Ethyl alcohol	2.90
m-Dinitrobenzene	1.08	Hydroquinone	3.27
Other nitro compounds	1.08	Methyl alcohol	3.35
p-Chloronitrobenzene	1.08	Urethan	3.50
Other nitro halides	1.08	Resorcinol	3.55
Pyridine	1.10	Acetamide	3.80
Pyrrole	1.10	Water	4.60

The values of these factors may also be determined graphically by the aid of a chart given in his first paper.

Mortimer finds that even polar substances may be included in this treatment with a fair degree of accuracy. Examples of the reverse calculation, of solubility from internal pressure, will be found in Chapter XIV.

Chapter X.

Solvation.

Negative deviations from Raoult's law and increased solubilities tend to occur when the components of a solution have that abnormally great attraction for each other which leads to the formation of solvates, or chemical compounds between solvent and solute.[1] This makes it important to utilize what knowledge is available concerning the factors which cause chemical combination in order to predict their effect upon solubility. The prediction of chemical combination is, however, the main goal of chemistry, and until it is reached the problem of solubility will likewise remain more or less unsolved. We must therefore be content to note a few guiding principles, together with a number of actual behaviors which may serve by analogy to predict others.

SOLVATION AND POLARITY.

From the discussion of polarity in Chapter VIII it is evident that chemical combination should be more frequent between molecules of high polarity than between those of low polarity, and examination of the experimental facts shows this to be the case. For example, the highly polar water molecule shows this tendency in a great degree, forming a great variety of hydrates, especially with the highly polar salt molecules. Other polar molecules, such as NH_3, furnish frequent instances of the same sort, for we have many ammonia complexes both in solution and in the solid state. The highly polar salts combine in great variety to form complex or double salts. Sulfuric and hydrofluoric acids enter into frequent combination with their salts.

As polarity diminishes this tendency diminishes also. "Alcohol of crystallization" occurs much less frequently than "water of crystallization," "benzene of crystallization" is known in comparatively few cases, while the nearly non-polar paraffin molecules almost never form addition compounds with other molecules.[2]

We may feel reasonably certain that the intermolecular attraction which yields solid "addition compounds" operates also in the liquid state to cause negative deviations from Raoult's law, so that the abundant existing evidence of the sort above cited justifies the statement that

[1] Cf. Chapter VII.
[2] G. N. Lewis, *J. Am. Chem. Soc.*, **35**, 1448 (1913); **38**, 762 (1916).

negative deviations from Raoult's law and abnormally great solubilities occur most frequently when the components are highly polar.

DIFFERENCE IN POSITIVE AND NEGATIVE CHARACTER OF THE COMPONENTS.

High polarity is not in itself sufficient to cause chemical combination. It is necessary for the substances to differ in the sense implied by the contrasting terms acidic and basic, or positive and negative. Thus, we usually think of water as a neutral substance, ammonia as positive or basic and HF as negative or acidic. Accordingly we find the affinity between water and NH_3 or water and HF to be much weaker than that between NH_3 and HF. Again, liquid NH_3 and liquid HCl, on mixing, would combine completely, giving the extreme negative deviation from Raoult's law. With ammonia and acetic acid the deviation is small, and with aniline and phenol it is very slight. (Table XI-5.)

The diversity in character which determines the tendency to addition or solvation may be interpreted in the sense of the "dualistic" theory of Davy and Berzelius, restated in modern terms. In the case of the elements the greatest tendency to form stable compounds occurs when one element is highly positive, readily losing electrons, and the other element highly negative, readily adding electrons. Arranging the elements according to decreasing tendency to lose electrons gives us the familiar "replacement series" of the elements, starting with the alkali metals and ending with the highly negative non-metallic elements. For purposes of discussion we may consider the following elements, arranged approximately according to their behavior towards electrons, K, Na, Ba, Ca, Mg, Zn, Fe, Pb, H, Cu, Ag, C, I, S, Br, Cl, O, F. The farther apart the elements in this series in general the more stable are their compounds. Those close together usually form either no compound, like oxygen and fluorine, sulfur and iodine, lead and copper, or one easily decomposed like chlorine and bromine, or carbon and iodine.

This same series, moreover, is significant in determining the combining tendencies of compounds.[3] The oxide of an element usually combines more strongly with the oxide of another according as the elements lie farther apart in the series. Thus H_2O combines but weakly with CuO, Ag_2O, CO_2, more strongly with SO_2 and SO_3 in one direction, and with MgO, CaO, BaO, K_2O in the other direction in the order named. The carbonates of K, Ba, Ca, Mg, Cu, give off CO_2 and leave the metallic oxide with increasing ease in the order named.

Other examples of this sort are given by Kendall[4] and collaborators in a series of very useful studies of the solubilities of polar substances,

[3] Cf. Hildebrand, "Principles of Chemistry," pp. 64-66, 72-73. Macmillan, 1920.
[4] Kendall, et al., loc. cit., p. 86.

wherein it is shown that the tendency of various salts to combine with or dissolve in their free acids is closely related to the separation of their metals from hydrogen in the potential series of the elements. It is shown, further, that a weak acid can act as a "base" towards a strong acid, the combination being stronger the greater the diversity in strength between the two acids. The strength of the combination may thus be regarded as dependent upon the negativity of the acid radicals. A fuller presentation of the results of these studies will be found in Chapter XV, where data upon the solubilities of polar substances are discussed in the light of preceding theories.

The phenomena just mentioned can be accounted for in terms of modern theories of atomic and molecular structure, advanced by G. N. Lewis.[5] Using the symbol of the element to indicate only the atomic kernel, and representing the valence electrons by dots, we have formulas for the free atoms such as the following:

$$\text{Na} \cdot \quad \text{Ca}: \quad : \text{Al} \cdot \quad \cdot \text{C}: \quad : \overset{\cdot}{\text{N}}: \quad : \overset{\cdot\cdot}{\text{O}}: \quad : \overset{\cdot}{\text{Cl}}:$$

The kernel in each case has a positive charge corresponding to its place in the Periodic System, and which, with the valence electrons, makes the net charge of the free atom zero. The electrons display a tendency to form octets around the atoms, and also a tendency to form pairs, and the nearly complete octet of the so-called negative or non-metallic elements can be completed by the addition of the loosely held electrons of the positive or metallic elements, which are then bound to the former by the resulting attraction of the positive metallic nucleus for the non-metallic atom with its extra electrons. The following formulas of familiar substances may serve for illustration

$$\text{Na}: \overset{\cdot\cdot}{\underset{\cdot\cdot}{\text{Cl}}}: \qquad \text{Ca}: \overset{\cdot\cdot}{\underset{\cdot\cdot}{\text{O}}}: \qquad \text{H}: \overset{\cdot\cdot}{\underset{\text{H}}{\text{N}}}: \text{H} \qquad \text{H}: \overset{\cdot\cdot}{\underset{\cdot\cdot}{\text{O}}}: \text{H}$$

$$: \overset{\cdot\cdot}{\text{O}}:$$
$$\overset{\cdot\cdot}{\underset{\cdot\cdot}{\text{S}}}: \overset{\cdot\cdot}{\underset{\cdot\cdot}{\text{O}}}: \qquad : \overset{\cdot\cdot}{\underset{\cdot\cdot}{\text{Cl}}}: \quad (\text{Cl}^-) \qquad \text{Ca} \quad (\text{Ca}^{++})$$
$$: \overset{}{\underset{\cdot\cdot}{\text{O}}}:$$

It will be noted that in molecules of SO_3 the atom of sulfur does not possess the full octet of electrons, which could, however, be completed by combination with CaO giving $CaSO_4$,

$$: \overset{\cdot\cdot}{\text{O}} \cdot$$
$$\text{Ca}: \overset{\cdot\cdot}{\text{O}}: \overset{\cdot\cdot}{\underset{\cdot\cdot}{\text{S}}}: \overset{\cdot\cdot}{\underset{\cdot\cdot}{\text{O}}}:$$
$$: \overset{}{\underset{\cdot\cdot}{\text{O}}}:$$

This tendency of SO_3 to add on the two additional electrons gives it the negative character of the old Berzelian doctrine, while the CaO,

[5] G. N. Lewis, *J. Am. Chem. Soc.*, **38**, 762 (1916).

which furnishes the necessary electrons is the positive oxide, just as Na is the positive element in NaCl because it furnishes the electron necessary to complete the octet about the atom of chlorine, making the latter negative.

It is evident, also, that since chromium has a smaller tendency to attract electrons than the more "negative" element, sulfur, the atom of chromium in CrO_3 would have a smaller tendency than does sulfur in SO_3 to complete its octet by adding CaO. Similarly, since the atom of barium has less tendency than that of calcium to hold on to its electrons, the molecule of BaO would more readily furnish the electrons to SO_3 necessary to complete the octet of sulfur. Hence $BaSO_4$ should dissociate into its component oxides less readily than $CaSO_4$.

COMPLEXES AND HYDRATES.

The formation of hydrates has an enormous effect upon the solubility of certain salts in water, the tendency to hydration appearing to be greatest with salts of metals at the top of the groups in the Periodic System, and diminishing as one descends the group. Thus LiCl, $MgCl_2$, $CaCl_2$, $ZnCl_2$ and $AlCl_3$ are deliquescent. On the other hand the tendency to form ammonia complexes is greatest for metals in the sub-groups and apparently increasing towards the bottom of the group [6] as illustrated by the familiar ammonia complexes with the ions of copper, silver, zinc, cobalt, nickel, etc., and the variety of ammono-basic [7] compounds with salts of mercury.

The nature of these combinations seems to be similar to that of the combinations discussed in the earlier paragraphs, in that electrons in the molecule of water or of ammonia seem able to fit into the coördination positions (which are usually twice the valence) of the ion. Silver ammonia ion would thus be represented by the electron formula

$$H \qquad\qquad H$$
$$H:\overset{..}{N}: \quad Ag \quad :\overset{..}{N}:H$$
$$H \qquad\qquad H$$

The reason for the preference of some ions for water and of others for ammonia is not very clear, but it may be connected with the fact that the water molecule is less basic than the ammonia molecule, the central oxygen atom drawing its electrons in closer than does the nitrogen atom of ammonia. Accordingly, we might conclude that the more negative water would tend to unite most strongly with the most positive ions or their salts, while the more positive ammonia would unite most strongly with the least positive ions or their salts. This distinction is obviously not entirely sufficient, however, to explain the facts.

The negative complexes can be treated in a similar manner. The firmest complex halides are formed by the halide of a very positive

---

[6] Hildebrand, *J. Am. Chem. Soc.*, **38**, 1471 (1916).
[7] Franklin, *Am. Chem. J.*, **47**, 285 (1912).

metal combining with the halide of a weakly positive metal, as in K_2PtCl_6 and K_2SiF_6, while the halides of metals near together display little or no tendency to unite.

UNSATURATED COMPOUNDS.

Molecules of unsaturated compounds are usually more polar than those of similar saturated compounds, as indicated by the criteria given in Chapter VIII, and so show a greater tendency to form addition compounds. In terms of the Lewis theory this may be due to the ability of such molecules to furnish the extra electrons required by certain other molecules to complete their octets or to fill their coördination positions. Ethylene, according to this theory, has the electron structure,

$$\begin{array}{cc} H & H \\ \ddot{C} :: \ddot{C} \\ \ddot{H} & \ddot{H} \end{array}$$

It may be possible to draw out the extra electron pair of the double bond to fill vacant spaces in other molecules, accounting for the formation of addition compounds.

Kendall, Crittenden and Miller,[8] in their rather extensive studies of compound formation in fused salt mixtures, have noted the great difference between antimony trihalides and aluminum trihalides in respect to the formation of compounds with other halides, the former being almost barren, the latter, particularly rich in this respect. This difference is beautifully correlated by the Lewis theory, with the difference in the charge of the atomic kernels of Al and Sb, which are 3 and 5, respectively, corresponding to their groups in the Periodic System. The electron structures of the trichlorides would accordingly be indicated as follows:

$$\begin{array}{cc} : \ddot{C}l : & : \ddot{C}l : \\ : \ddot{C}l : Al & : \ddot{C}l : \ddot{S}b : \\ : \ddot{C}l : & : \ddot{C}l : \end{array}$$

The Sb has its complete octet of electrons, and both it and the chlorine atoms are saturated. On the other hand, the Al has but 6 electrons and can attach 2 more. For example, with KCl it forms the compound

$$\begin{array}{c} : \ddot{C}l : \\ : \ddot{C}l : Al : \ddot{C}l : K \\ : \ddot{C}l : \end{array}$$

which, in the fused state, would doubtless contain the anion $AlCl_4^-$.

[8] Kendall, Crittenden and Miller, *J. Am. Chem. Soc.*, **45**, 963 (1923).

Compounds containing more $AlCl_3$ can be found by a union of $AlCl_3$ molecules, which may be represented as follows:

$$: \ddot{C}l : \quad : \ddot{C}l : \quad : \ddot{C}l :$$
$$: \ddot{C}l : \ddot{A}l : \ddot{C}l : \ddot{A}l : \ddot{C}l : \ddot{A}l$$
$$: \ddot{C}l : \quad : \ddot{C}l : \quad : \ddot{C}l :$$

This union may be continued indefinitely in pure $AlCl_3$, fixing the positions of the $AlCl_3$ molecules, and giving a solid rather than a liquid, on account of the orienting forces, although one which is volatile on account of the weakness of these forces.

In $SbCl_3$, the orienting forces are weaker, so that it can exist as a liquid through a considerable temperature range, and, for similar reasons, it shows but little tendency to form double salts. We might expect this difference between the halides of Al and Sb to cause many differences in solubility. We would probably find, for example, that solid $AlCl_3$ would be more soluble in chlorobenzene than would solid $SbCl_3$, if the solids were compared at temperatures at which their activities with respect to their liquid forms are equal.

There is reason to hope that the attention now being paid to atomic and molecular structure will lead to rapid advances in our ability to predict combination of the more unusual types than those treated above, which will be very important for the theory of solubility, for though the simple principles just outlined accord fairly well with a considerable amount of solubility data, as will be seen in subsequent chapters, there will be found many cases which are still quite baffling.

Chapter XI.

Vapor Pressures of Liquid Mixtures.

PARTIAL VAPOR PRESSURES.

Having discussed in the preceding chapter the various factors which affect solubility, it is our purpose in this and subsequent chapters to consider the experimental data in the light of the theory, and to see how far the theory can be trusted, in its present stage of development, to explain the facts and to serve as a basis for prediction of new facts. Having decided to define the ideal solution by the aid of Raoult's law, which relates composition to vapor pressure or to fugacity, it seems appropriate to make our first applications of the general theory of solubility to the vapor pressures of liquid mixtures, although it must be confessed, at the outset, that the data at hand are less extensive and accurate than those available for other solutions, particularly those of solids.

In Chapter V the deviation from ideality for certain mixtures was expressed in terms of log a/N. We may now re-examine these and other mixtures investigated by Zawidzski by the same method, with the results shown in Table 1.

In the first case we have a considerable deviation due to the large internal pressure difference, and in the second, due to the polarity of acetone. The relative deviations in the last three cases are in harmony with the order of increasing internal pressure, ethyl acetate, carbon tetrachloride, benzene, ethyl iodide.

TOTAL VAPOR PRESSURES AND BOILING POINT-COMPOSITION CURVES.

Most of the available data have reference to the relation of boiling point to composition, and do not give the composition of the vapor, so that it is not possible to calculate the deviation from Raoult's law

TABLE 1.

DEVIATIONS FROM RAOULT'S LAW, WHEN $N = 0.5$.

X_1 X_2	Log a_1/N_1	Log a_2/N_2	Temp.
Carbondisulfide-methylal	0.125	0.085	35.2°
Carbondisulfide-acetone	0.20	0.145	35.2°
Carbontetrachloride-benzene	0.020	0.016	50°
Carbontetrachloride-ethylacetate	0.036	0.026	50°
Ethyliodide-ethylacetate	0.047	0.050	50°

TABLE 2.

Deviation of Benzene Solutions from Raoult's Law.

Second Liquid	Percent Deviation	Temp.
Hexane	+ 11	70°
Ethyl ether	− 1.2	40°
Stannic chloride	+ 35	30°
Toluene	+ 9	40°
Carbon tetrachloride	+ 3.5	50°
Chloroform ....:................	− 0.6	20°
Benzene ....:	0	...
Ethylene chloride	+ 0	50°
Carbon disulfide	+ 10	20°
	+ 7.5	40°
Ethyl alcohol	+ 60	40°

of the separate components. It is, therefore, necessary to express the deviation in terms of the total pressure. When the vapor pressure curves of the pure components are known, we can calculate the ideal total vapor pressure by the expression $p_1°N_1 + p_2°N_2$. Equation IV-1. Subtracting this from the pressure under which the mixture actually boils we get the deviation from ideality, which may best be expressed in terms of percent of the ideal pressure. This procedure yielded the figures in the first column of Table VI-1, and which we may now examine further in the light of Chapters VII to X.

The fullest data illustrating the relation between deviations and internal pressures are furnished by mixtures in which benzene is one component, shown in Table 2, in which the other components have been arranged in order of internal pressure. The temperatures are not uniform, so that the usual effect of higher temperatures in inducing an approach to normal behavior should be borne in mind.

The magnitude of the deviations increases, in general, as the internal pressure (and with alcohol the polarity) of the second component differs from that of benzene. The only important exception is with ether, where we may assume that a tendency towards combination overcomes the effect of internal pressure. As solvents for other substances, ether and benzene usually differ considerably.

Carbon disulfide mixtures also show deviations in harmony with differences in internal pressure with other liquids of low polarity, and with the large difference in polarity, in the case of acetone, as illustrated by the summary in Table 3.

TABLE 3.

Deviations of Carbon Disulfide Solutions from Raoult's Law.

Second Liquid	Percent Deviation	Temperature
Methylal	22	25°
Chloroform	17	20°
Benzene	10	20°
Carbon disulfide	0	...
Acetone	35	35°

Other comparisons may be made with the data in Table VI-1, yielding good, though not perfect agreement with predictions based upon theory. Certain other cases are also of interest. In Chapter XII, the solubilities of chlorine will be discussed, which, though ordinarily regarded as a gas, might equally well be discussed in the present chapter. It will be seen that it dissolves in carbon tetrachloride, for example, nearly to the extent demanded by Raoult's law. On the other hand bromine, whose internal pressure is much greater, shows a strong positive deviation in carbon tetrachloride solution according to Lewis and Storch,[1] giving $p_1/p_2° = 0.048$ when $N_2 = 0.025$.

Constant Boiling Mixtures—Minimum Boiling Points.

When the two components of a binary mixture have nearly equal vapor pressures it takes little positive deviation from Raoult's law to yield a maximum in the vapor pressure composition curve, which is a condition of great practical significance, since it limits the possibility of separation by fractional distillation. Where the components differ considerably in internal pressure or in polarity, a mixture with a minimum boiling point may be found, even when the boiling points of the pure components differ considerably.

A large number of liquid mixtures have been examined by Lecat for maxima and minima in boiling points, and his own observations, together with a remarkably complete record of similar observations by others are to be found in his book, "La Tension de Vapeur des Melanges de Liquides: L'Azeotropisme";[2] a work indispensable to anyone concerned with the problems of distillation. Table 4 gives several examples from these collected data.

Cyclohexane is not far enough from hexane to yield a minimum boiling mixture in view of the difference of 12° in their boiling points,

TABLE 4.
Minimum Boiling Liquid Mixtures.

X_1	b. pt.	X_2	b. pt.	Min. b. pt. of mixture
Cyclohexane	80.8°	Hexane	69.0°	None
"	....	Carbon tetrachloride ...	76.8°	76.5°
"	....	Toluene	110.7°	None
"	....	Benzene	80.2°	77.5°
"	....	Methylethyl ketone....	79.6°	72
Carbon tetrachloride	76.8°	Diethyl ketone	102.2°	None
"	....	Cyclohexane	80.8°	76.5°
"	....	Ethyl acetate	77.2°	74.8°
Mesitylene	164.0°	Benzene	78.0°	None
"	....	Chlorotoluene	161.3°	160.5°
"	....	Bromobenzene	156.1°	None
"	....	Propionic acid	140.7°	139.3°

[1] Lewis and Storch, *J. Am. Chem. Soc.*, **39**, 2544 (1917).
[2] Brussels, Lamertin, 1918.

but carbon tetrachloride, farther from cyclohexane in internal pressure and nearer in boiling point, gives a mixture boiling with a slight minimum. Toluene, with its much higher boiling point shows no minimum although the deviation from Raoult's law is doubtless equally large. Benzene, differing still more in internal pressure and with nearly the same boiling point shows a pronounced minimum. Methyl ethyl ketone on account of its polarity shows a still more pronounced minimum, while diethyl ketone, though nearly as polar and undoubtedly deviating almost as much from Raoult's law has a boiling point so much higher that no minimum appears.

Carbon tetrachloride differs but little in boiling point from the three other liquids mentioned with it in Table 4, but cyclohexane and ethyl acetate differ enough from it in internal pressure (and the latter probably in polarity as well) to give minimum boiling mixtures, while benzene, which it resembles more closely does not.

Mesitylene and chlorotoluene have boiling points close together, so that their small difference in internal pressure is sufficient to give a minimum. Bromo-benzene, though having a larger internal pressure, boils enough lower than mesitylene to give no minimum boiling mixture, while propionic acid, though boiling still lower, is so polar a substance that a minimum again appears.

CONSTANT BOILING MIXTURES—MAXIMUM BOILING POINTS.

Negative deviations from Raoult's law result from tendency towards chemical union, and when this is sufficiently marked to counteract any difference in boiling points of the pure components it may give rise to a minimum in the vapor pressure curve and a maximum in the boiling point curve. The following cases of minimum vapor pressure have already been mentioned, chloroform-acetone (pp. 42, 63); chloroform-ether (p. 63). The former gives a maximum boiling point, as shown in Table 5, while the latter, by reason of the difference of 26.4° in the boiling points of the pure constituents, is not able to show a maximum.

Further examples from Lecat are given in Table 5, which illustrate certain of the principles earlier outlined (p. 84). They illustrate the fact that negative deviations from Raoult's law occur almost exclusively with polar substances, and also that a pronounced difference in acidic and basic character promotes such deviation. Thus, aniline and hydrogen chloride give a very great maximum in boiling point, while aniline and the weaker acetic acid, in spite of the much smaller difference in their boiling points, do not give a maximum boiling mixture. Propionic acid with pyridine, a stronger base than aniline, shows a maximum 10° higher than the boiling point of the acid. It should be noted that not all the substances showing this evidence of combination are commonly regarded as acidic and basic respectively, for the list contains such polar substances as ketones, esters and aldehydes.

FRACTIONAL DISTILLATION.

The method for constructing the boiling point-composition curve from the vapor pressure curves of the pure components and upon the assumption of Raoult's law has already been described (IV). When deviations from ideality occur they give rise to corresponding deviations in the boiling point curve, causing greater separation between the two curves, as in IV—Fig. 2. The deviation may be sufficient, provided the difference in boiling points is not too great, to give a minimum, in which case the vapor tends to approach the composition of the minimum boiling mixture and no complete separation of the components is possible, unless the minimum can be destroyed by distilling under a different pressure, or perhaps by adding a third component.

Conversely, when the deviation from Raoult's law is negative the boiling point-composition curve may show a maximum, in which case the distillate will contain an excess of one component or the other, depending upon which side of the maximum the mixture lies. In either case, the residue will approach in composition the maximum boiling mixture and no complete fractionation will be possible unless the maximum can be destroyed.

MOLECULAR WEIGHT FROM RISE IN BOILING POINT.

The rise in the boiling point of a solvent per mol of solute has been extensively used to determine the molecular weight of the solute. In most cases, however, there is found a departure from the normal value as the concentration of the solute is increased, in spite of care taken to express the concentration in the most favorable way. This departure has invited calculations of the "degree of association," and so great has been the faith of most investigators in the validity of the

TABLE 5.
MAXIMUM BOILING LIQUID MIXTURES.

X_1	b. pt.	X_2	b. pt.	Max. b. pt. of mixture
Chloroform	61.0°	Acetone	56.3°	63.4°
"	....	Ether	34.6°	None
Water	100.0°	Hydrogen chloride	—80°	110°
"	....	Nitric acid	86°	120.5°
Pyridine	115.5°	Propionic acid	140.7°	150.8°
Phenol	181.5°	Glycol	197.4°	199°
"	....	Benzene aldehyde	179.2°	185.6°
"	....	Aniline	184.4°	186.2°
"	....	Ethyl butyrate	178.6°	185.6°
"	....	Benzyl alcohol	205.5°	206°
Formic acid	100.8°	Acetone	56.2°	None
" "	....	Diethyl ketone	102.2°	105.0°
Aniline	184.4°	Hydrogen chloride	—80°	244.8°
"	....	Acetic acid	118.5°	None

boiling point law that it has seldom occurred to them to put the onus for any departure upon it rather than upon the molecular weight. The theories outlined in this volume do not lead us to expect that many substances will form wholly ideal solutions or give constant and normal values of molecular weight, even though their molecular weights as pure liquids are quite normal.

The rise in boiling point for a solution which obeys Raoult's law can be obtained by substituting Equation III-16 in VI-2 and remembering that for such a solution the heat of mixing is 0, so that the heat of vaporization from the solution is the same as for the pure solvent (Equation VI-5). This gives

$$\frac{d \ln N_1}{dT} = \frac{L_1}{RT^2} = \frac{1}{N_1}\frac{dN_1}{dT}. \tag{1}$$

Here dT is the rise in boiling point for a reduction in the solvent concentration of dN_1. We may write $dN_2 = -dN_1$ and call $N_1 = 1$ for dilute solutions, getting the more familiar approximate expression

$$\frac{RT^2}{L} = -\frac{dT}{dN_2}. \tag{2}$$

We may illustrate departures from the ideal solution law by comparing the rise in boiling point of carbon disulfide produced respectively by naphthalene and phosphorus, according to data by Beckmann.[3] The values of L for the solvent given in the literature are 6670,[4] 6420,[5] 6380,[6] 6600,[7] the mean of which is 6520. This gives $RT^2/L = 30.8$. Table 6 gives part of the original data, together with values of N_2 and of $\Delta T/N_2$. It will be noted that the molal rise in boiling point with naphthalene solutions is but little less than the normal value, whereas, with phosphorus it is considerably less for similar concentrations. This difference is in harmony with the internal pressure differences and with data mentioned elsewhere upon the solubilities of these same solutes in carbon disulfide.

If the molal weight of the solute, instead of the molal rise, is calculated from the data, we obtain the values in the last column of the table, which might be interpreted to mean that naphthalene is slightly associated in carbon disulfide while phosphorus is considerably so. Such an assumption the author believes to be without foundation, for the components of the solution are so unlike that they form two liquid phases below $-6.5°$ (cf. XIII) and must also be far from ideal at the boiling point of carbon disulfide. It is the equation, therefore, not the molecular weight of phosphorus, which needs correction.

[3] Beckmann, *Z. physik. Chem.*, **6**, 437 (1890); **5**, 76 (1890).
[4] Regnault, *Mem. Acad.*, **26**, 1, 262 (1862).
[5] Winkelmann, *Ann. d. Physik*, **9**, 208, 368 (1880).
[6] Wirtz, *ibid.*, **40**, 446 (1890).
[7] Andrews, *Pogg. Ann.*, **75**, 501 (1848).

TABLE 6.

RISE IN BOILING POINT OF CARBON DISULFIDE.

Solute	N_2	ΔT	$\Delta T / N_2$	Apparent molec. wt.
Ideal	....	....	30.8	......
Naphthalene	0.0438	1.293	29.5	1.04 x 128
"	0.0762	2.268	29.8	1.03 x 128
Phosphorus	0.0339	0.980	28.8	1.07 x 124
"	0.0681	1.810	26.6	1.16 x 124
"	0.1032	2.630	25.4	1.21 x 124

We may further object to the frequent practice of making the molecular weight of the solute bear the brunt of the entire alteration required to make the data fit the ideal equation, even in cases where the solvent is polar and the solute non-polar, and where association of the former might more properly be assumed. It should be remembered, as pointed out in Chapter V, that association of either component would cause both to deviate in a positive direction from Raoult's law, and hence the fact that such deviation may be found should not be taken as evidence that the solute is associated rather than the solvent. For example, one observer has concluded that anthracene is associated in solution in fused cinnamic acid, although the latter is surely far more polar than the former, and hence should be regarded as the associated component. In the light of the preceding paragraphs, however, we do not believe that an "association factor" obtained by reversing the calculation would have any quantitative significance.

Chapter XII.

Solubilities of Gases.

Since the solubility of a gas below its critical temperature is simply the converse of the partial vapor pressure of the gas from its solution, it is but a step from the topic of the preceding chapter to the topic of this. For example, the solubility of chlorine gas under, say, one atmosphere pressure, is identical with the mol fraction of liquid chlorine that would have to be taken in a solution to give a partial vapor pressure of chlorine equal to one atmosphere. The consequences of Raoult's law when applied to the solubility of gases were given in Chapter IV, and it is now appropriate to consider the existing solubility data in order to determine how far departures from Raoult's law accord with the theoretical considerations set forth in Chapters VII to X.[1]

GASES OF LOW POLARITY.

The simplest solutions are, of course, those in which chemical reactions between solvent and solute are absent, and so we may advantageously consider first the solubilities of a number of non-polar gases in a series of liquids chiefly of low polarity. A large part of the available data upon systems of this class are summarized in Table 1, together with the dielectric constants of the solvents to serve as rough indications of their polarities (cf. Chapter VIII). An approximate figure for the ideal solubility at one atmosphere partial pressure has been calculated by the aid of Raoult's law, as explained in Chapter IV, except in the case of hydrogen, where the extrapolation of $p°$ to ordinary temperatures would have to be over such a wide range as to rob the result of nearly all significance.

The values for hydrogen, nitrogen, and carbon monoxide are by Just,[2] for the hydrocarbons by Mc Daniel,[3] for oxygen by Fischer and Pfleiderer,[4] for chlorine by N. W. Taylor,[5] for phosgene by Atkinson, Heycock and Pope,[6] and for niton by Schulze[7] and by

---

[1] Cf. Hildebrand, *J. Am. Chem. Soc.*, **38**, 1452 (1916); Taylor and Hildebrand, *ibid.*, **45**, 682 (1923).
[2] Just, *Z. physik. Chem.*, **37**, 342 (1901).
[3] McDaniel, *J. phys. Chem.*, **15**, 587 (1911).
[4] Fischer and Pfleiderer, *Z. anorg. Allgem. Chem.*, **124**, 61 (1922).
[5] N. W. Taylor and Hildebrand, loc. cit.
[6] Atkinson, Heycock and Pope, *J. Chem. Soc.*, **117**, 1410 (1920).
[7] Schulze, *Z. phys. Chem.*, **95**, 257 (1920).

TABLE 1.

SOLUBILITIES OF GASES. MOL PERCENT.

Solvent	Dielec. Const.	H_2 20°	N_2 20°	CO 20°	O_2 16°–20°	CH_4 25°	C_2H_4 25°	Cl_2 0°	Cl_2 40°	$COCl_2$ 24°	N+ 20°
Ideal (1/p°)	1.0	...	0.10	0.11	0.16 (20°)	0.32	1.48	27.3	8.7	55	6.92
Hexane	1.9	...	...	...	...	0.31	1.59	...	...	...	7.95
Heptane	1.9	...	...	...	...	...	...	27.0	...	...	...
Ether	4.3	...	...	...	0.19 (20°)	...	...	...	...	...	6.03
Silicon tetrachloride	2.4	...	...	...	...	...	...	28.8	...	...	...
Amyl acetate	4.8	0.046	0.094	0.13	...	...	...	...	...	...	7.80
Cyclohexane	2.1	...	...	...	...	...	...	...	...	...	2.77
Ethyl acetate	6.1	0.032	0.068	0.099	...	0.26	...	...	...	...	5.85
m-Xylene	2.3	0.040	0.061	0.089	0.093 (16°)	...	...	...	...	53	...
Carbon tetrachloride	2.2	...	...	...	0.099 (18°)	0.21	...	29.6	12.2	...	5.20
Toluene	2.3	0.037	0.053	0.077	0.082 (18°)	...	...	...	...	53	4.68
Chloroform	5.1	...	0.043	0.063	0.073 (16°)	...	...	...	...	...	1.85
Acetone	22	0.021	0.042	0.065	0.068 (19°)	0.18	0.75	...	...	...	4.31
Benzene	1.9	0.026	0.041	0.061	0.065 (19°)	...	1.25	...	...	54	...
Chlorobenzene	11.0	...	...	...	...	0.18	...	...	...	...	...
Ethylene bromide	4.9	...	...	...	...	...	...	...	11.9	...	...
Ethyl alcohol	26	0.021	0.033	0.045	...	0.11	...	...	...	...	1.44
Nitrobenzene	35	0.015	0.026	0.039	0.032 (18°)	...	...	...	...	...	...
Methyl alcohol	31	0.015	0.022	0.030	...	0.074	...	...	...	...	5.56
Carbon bisulfide	2.6	...	0.013	0.020	...	...	...	...	...	...	...
Aniline	7.3	0.012	0.011	0.019	...	...	...	...	...	...	1.41
Water	80	0.0015	0.0013	0.0019	0.0017 (20°)	0.024	0.084	0.75	0.31	...	0.02

Remstedt.[8] Chlorine and phosgene are far from being non-polar, but can be included in this table because of their normal behavior with the particular solvents chosen.

The solvents have been listed in the table in the order of increasing internal pressure, as given by the various methods outlined in Chapter IX, the polar solvents, however, being listed in the positions corresponding to their solvent powers as the solubility falls off from top to bottom of the table. The methods for calculating relative internal pressures are not very significant when applied to highly polar substances, and do not agree very well as to the position of such liquids in the internal pressure series, though the agreement is better for a substance like aniline, where the polarity is not great, than it is for such liquids as acetone and the alcohols. We shall see later that the liquids of low polarity in the table maintain the same order with other solutes, while the highly polar liquids do not. In other words, the solvent powers of the polar liquids are far more specific. Nevertheless the regularity in the positions of the polar liquids in the table with respect to all the gases for which we have data indicates that the series given is of considerable value for predicting solubilities of other inert gases, or for filling in the gaps in the table. For example we may predict that the solubility of oxygen in ethyl alcohol would be about 0.052, although with less confidence than if the solvent were non-polar.

The most striking feature of the table is that the regular decrease in solubility from top to bottom is maintained with but few irregularities for all the gases shown with the exception of chlorine and phosgene. This accords with the fact that the liquefied gases have low internal pressures. Table 2 gives figures indicating the relative internal pressures of N_2, CO, A, and O_2 at — 203° C., at which temperature we have data for surface tensions, densities, and coefficients of expansion.[9] These data, together with the van der Waals a, and the heats of vaporization L, calculated from the vapor pressure [10] can be applied as shown in Chapter IX. The values in the last four columns not only increase regularly, but by comparison with the internal pressure data in Chapter IX are seen to be of the same order of magnitude as those for the solvents at the top of Table 1, so that at ordinary temperatures these gases may be regarded as showing the behavior of substances of very low internal pressures, and solutions even in the liquids near the top of Table 1 should show a positive deviation from Raoult's law, and, therefore, solubilities somewhat less than the ideal, and falling off as we proceed to solvents of higher internal pressure. Allowing for the very approximate nature of the ideal values in Table 1 it will be seen that the theory is well substantiated.

Methane and ethylene, with their higher boiling points, undoubtedly

[8] Remstedt, *Le Radium*, **8**, 253 (1911).
[9] Baly and Donnan, *J. Chem. Soc.*, **81**, 907 (1902).
[10] Cf. Hildebrand, *J. Am. Chem. Soc.*, **41**, 1073 (1919).

TABLE 2.

RELATIVE INTERNAL PRESSURES AT — 203° C.

	T_b	γ	$a \cdot 10^4$	$a \cdot 10^5$	v	$\dfrac{\gamma}{v^{1/3}}$	$\dfrac{L\text{-}RT}{v}$	$\dfrac{a}{v^2} \cdot 10^8$	$\dfrac{1}{v}\left(\dfrac{1}{a}+140\right)$
N₂	77.3	10.53	27	560	33.4	3.28	24.2	243	10.2
CO	83	12.84	28	491	33.1	4.00	29.4	262	10.4
A	87	13.63	26	450	26.3	4.59	40.7	390	13.8
O₂	90	18.35	27	385	25.8	6.22	44.6	410	15.5

have higher internal pressures in the liquid state, and it is not surprising to find the solubility in hexane correspond with the ideal within the limit of error, but falling off as before towards the bottom of the table. The ideal value calculated for niton is less than the experimental value in hexane, but the necessary uncertainties in the data for such a gas make this of little moment. However, the relative accuracy is surely better than the absolute accuracy, and the solubilities given fall off regularly with but two exceptions, cyclohexane (or ether?) and carbon disulfide. The slight polarity of the ether may give it a smaller solvent power for a very non-polar substance like niton. The latter 'discrepancy is far more serious. Not only the solubilities of nitrogen and carbon monoxide, but also those of iodine, sulfur, phosphorus, p-dibromobenzene, phenanthrene and anthracene (cf. Chap. XV) agree in placing carbon disulfide low down in the solubility series, so that a different position with reference to niton, if the experimental data can be trusted, is very surprising. It may prove to be related to another at present inexplicable behavior of carbon disulfide. The author noted in his third paper upon solubility that the position of this liquid indicated by $T(\partial P/\partial T)_v$ was different from its position according to all other methods for estimating internal pressure. Comparing it with benzene, for example, we get the following figures.

	$T\left(\dfrac{\partial P}{\partial T}\right)_V$	$\dfrac{a}{v^2} \cdot 10^8$	$\dfrac{\gamma}{v^{1/3}}$	$\dfrac{L-RT}{v}$	$\dfrac{1/a+2T}{v}$	Sutherland
Benzene	3810	472	6.5	86	1.56	556
Carbon bisulfide	3840	610	8.7	109	2.27	743

The ratios of the two values in each of the last five columns is nearly the same, 1.4, indicating that these liquids have by no means identical internal pressures, as would seem to be the case from the first pair of values. The situation calls for further experimental checks of the data, or perhaps for an examination of the factors suggested in Equation VI-25 as modifying the indications of internal pressure alone.

Liquid chlorine seems to have an internal pressure near that of benzene (T IX-2 and 5), so that the ideal solubility should be shown in solvents in this region of the table, with lower solubilities not only in the liquids lower down but in those higher up as well, a behavior quite different from that shown by the previous gases. The values in Table 1 show that this is the case. The small solubility in water, in spite of the hydrolysis of part of the chlorine, is due, as with the other gases, to the very high polarity and cohesion of the water.

The ideal solubility can be calculated from $p°$, the vapor pressure of liquid chlorine at the temperature in question, but since the necessary data exist it is interesting, in this case, to use the fugacities of chlorine at 1 atmosphere and at the saturation pressure, respectively, calculating the ideal solubility from the Equation III-11, $N_2 = f_2/f_2°$.

Taking the weight of one liter of chlorine at 0° C. and at 100° C. as 3.220 grams and 2.329 grams respectively, we calculate α in Equation III-6 to be 380 cc. and 160 cc. respectively. Interpolation gives α = 335 cc. at 20° C. and α = 290 cc. at 40° C. From these values we have prepared the following table:

TABLE 3.

IDEAL CHLORINE SOLUBILITIES.

Temp.	Press.[11] $p°$	Fugacity when $p = 1$	when $p = p°$	Mol percent calc. from $1/p° = N$	from $f/f° = N$
0° C.	3.66 at.	0.984 at.	3.44 at.	27.3	28.6
20° C.	6.62	0.986	6.04	15.1	16.34
40° C.	11.50	0.989	10.1	8.7	9.79

It will be noticed that these "ideal" values do not differ much from those actually obtained. That Raoult's law is obeyed closely in very dilute chlorine solutions in CCl_4 at 0° C. is shown by the vapor pressures measurements of Jakowkin.[12] A comparison of our calculated $f/f°$ with his observed values of N is given below. It will be noted that N agrees a little better with $f/f°$ than with $p/p°$.

TABLE 4.

N_2	0.00086	0.00225	0.00423	0.00718
$p/p°$	0.00092	0.00208	0.00410	0.00673
$f/f°$	0.00098	0.00221	0.00436	0.00716

In the following chapter will be found data upon the lowering of the freezing point of chlorine by the addition of other liquids which confirm the increase in solubility here shown as we approach the liquids in the middle of the table.

Turning to the case of phosgene, we find that it dissolves with almost equal readiness in xylene, toluene and chlorobenzene. This is to be expected if liquid phosgene has about the same internal pressure as toluene. The value of the expression $\dfrac{5200 + 30\,t_b}{v_{20}}$ is 76.4 for $COCl_2$ and 80.0 for toluene. The difference is not great. The corresponding value for nitrobenzene is 113.0. This high value is in accordance with the fact that it gives low phosgene solubilities.

[11] Vapor pressure data from Knietsch, *Wied. Ann.*, **259**, 124 (1899). His measurements are in good agreement with those of Johnson and McIntosh, *J. Am. Chem. Soc.*, **31**, 1140 (1909).

[12] Cf. Hildebrand, *J. Am. Chem. Soc.*, **38**, 1465 (1916).

It has, however, a very high dielectric constant, 35, so that its polarity should also greatly affect its solvent power.

The parallelism between the values for the first four gases in Table 1 corresponds to a useful generalization given by Just,[13] that the ratio of the solubilities of two gases is constant in all solvents. The table makes it evident, however, that this is true only where the two gases show the maximum, or ideal solubility in the same region of the table. Chlorine and nitrogen, for example, would not show this constant ratio.

AMMONIA.

Turning to cases where polarity plays an important rôle, we may consider first the meager data available upon the solubilities of ammonia gas, as follows:

TABLE 5.
MOL FRACTION OF NH_3 GAS AT 1 ATMOS. DISSOLVING AT 0°.

Ideal [14]	Toluene [15]	Ether [16]	Ethyl [17] alcohol	Methyl [17] alcohol	Water [18]
0.238	0.0026	0.079	0.398	0.439	0.481

Ammonia being a highly polar substance, as shown by its high dielectric constant and solvent power for salts when it is in the liquid state, as well as by its general chemical reactivity, it is not at all strange to find that, like water, it is but slightly soluble in toluene, more so in the slightly polar ether, the solubility increasing further as we proceed in order to the more polar ethyl alcohol, methyl alcohol and finally water, where the chemical properties of the solution show that a reaction has taken place, forming some NH_4^+ and OH^-.

CARBON DIOXIDE AND NITROUS OXIDE.

A considerable amount of data has been obtained for the solubilities of these gases by Just [19] and by Kunerth,[20] most of which is summarized in Table 6. The solvents are arranged in the same order as was used in Table 1 to give a decreasing series of solubilities and internal pressures, several other solvents being now added in positions according to their internal pressures shown in the second and third columns of figures. The four solvents following water at the bottom are not part of the series.

The ideal solubilities of these gases at 1 atmosphere calculated from the relation $N = 1/p°$ can be calculated from their saturation pressures at 20° which, according to Villard,[21] are 56.3 atm., for CO_2

[13] Just, Z. physik. Chem., 37, 342 (1901).
[14] From $N = 1/p°$, taking $p° = 4.19$ atm.
[15] Calculated from data by Hantzsch and Vagt.
[16] De Bruyn, Rec. trav. chim., 11, 112 (1892).
[17] Mallet, Am. Chem. Journ., 19, 807 (1897).
[18] Perman, J. Chem. Soc., 83, 1168 (1903).
[19] Just. Z. physik. Chem., 37, 342 (1901).
[20] Kunerth, Phys. Rev., 19, 519 (1922).
[21] Villard, Ann. chim. phys. [7], 10, 387 (1897).

TABLE 6.

SOLUBILITIES OF CO_2 AND N_2O AT $20°$.

Solvents	Dielectric Constant	$\dfrac{\gamma}{v^{1/3}}$	$\dfrac{5200 + 30t}{v}$	Mol fractions $\times 10^4$		
				$CO_2(J)$	$CO_2(K)$	$N_2O(K)$
Amyl acetate	4.8	4.5	65	270	283	312
Xylene	2.3	5.6	76	102	...	...
Carbon tetrachloride	2.2	5.8	78	100	...	...
Toluene	2.2	6.1	80	107	...	...
Chloroform	5.1	6.2	88	123	121	182
Acetone	22	5.5	94	209	...	...
Benzene	2.3	6.5	86	91	...	...
Chlorobenzene	11	7.0	90	93	...	...
Benzyl chloride	...	...	91	90	...	...
Bromobenzene	5.2	7.5	94	77	...	...
Iodobenzene	4.6	7.8	97	60	...	...
Ethylene chloride	10.4	7.5	98	125	...	...
Ethylene bromide	4.9	8.7	106	82	82	100
Ethyl alcohol	26	5.7	109	70	69	72
Nitrobenzene	35	10	110	113	...	...
Methyl alcohol	31	6.8	84	71	60	53
Carbon bisulfide	2.6	8.7	109	22	...	...
Aniline	7.3	10	117	55	53	· 56
Water	80	28	450	7	7	5
o-Toluidine	5.9	8	105	66	...	...
Pyridine	12.0	9	107	129	129	120
Acetic acid	10	7.4	153	121	124	115
Benzaldehyde ..,......	18	8.4	104	128	125	134
Ideal, $1/p°$	...	...	...	...	178	202
$1/f°$	...	...	...	...	254	...

and 49.4 atm. for N_2O, giving for N, 0.0178 and 0.0202, respectively. Since the above pressures are very high, making the gases deviate considerably from the gas laws, it may be preferable to calculate N from $1/f°$. Roth[22] has given data for the ratio of the volume of CO_2 at $18.5°$ under various pressures, to the volume at $0°$ and 1 atm., and Rayleigh has measured the density of the gas at $0°$ and 1 atm., from which the volume per mol is found to be 22.34 liters. Using this value we may give the actual molal volumes instead of the relative volumes given by Roth, as follows:

TABLE 7.

p	v	v_4	$\alpha = v^4 - v$
10	2.065	2.241	176
15	1.350	1.492	142
20	0.989	1.121	132
25	0.729	0.896	167
30	0.592	0.720	128
35	0.490	0.640	150
40	0.398	0.560	162
45	0.335	0.498	163

Av. 152

[22] Roth, *Wied. Ann.*, **11**, 1 (1880).

The ideal volumes at the same pressures are given in the 3rd column while the 4th gives their difference, α in Equation III-6. Using Equation III-8 we calculate

$$2.3 \log f/56.3 = \frac{-152 \times 56.3}{82 \times 293} = -0.356,$$

whence $f = 39.3$ atm., and the ideal solubility would be $1/39.3 = 0.0254$.

Dolezalek has "corrected" the saturation pressure by substituting for it $p + a/v^2$, which, taking $a = 0.0070$, gives 120 atm., which gives for the solubility $1/120 = 0.00835$, a very different figure from either $1/p$ or $1/f$. Of course, $p + a/v^2$ would represent the ideal pressure only if b were zero, which is by no means the case.

There are no very satisfactory data for estimating the internal pressures of either CO_2 or N_2O in the liquid form, so we cannot well decide whether the solubility in liquids of low internal pressure, such as xylene and carbon tetrachloride, represents the maximum or ideal value, or whether this would be found in liquids of still lower internal pressure. It seems evident that the value calculated by Dolezalek is too low, for a number of normal liquids at the top of the table show much greater solvent powers, higher than $1/(p° + a/v^2)$ but lower than both $1/p°$ and $1/f°$. It is not very important, therefore, to determine which of the two latter expressions has the practical advantage.

The chemical behavior of CO_2 indicates that it has a very appreciable polarity. Its ready union with various oxides to form carbonates would indicate the possibility of its uniting more or less generally with polar compounds. On the other hand, the fact that it is by no means highly polar would tend to make it adhere to the same solubility series with liquids of low polarity as was shown in Table 1 by the more inert gases. It will be noted, accordingly, that the solvents in Table 6, which have low dielectric constants, and from which very polar bonds are absent, show solvent powers for CO_2 falling off regularly, almost within the obviously considerable limit of error, as the bottom of the main portion of the table is approached. Polarity in the solvent, however, causes an abnormally high solubility, as illustrated by amyl acetate, acetone, ethylene chloride, aniline and nitrobenzene, and to a lesser degree by the alcohols, chlorobenzene and chloroform. Thus aniline, which was a slightly poorer solvent for N_2 and CO than carbon disulfide, is a much better solvent for CO_2, due to its polarity and its basic character. Doubly bound oxygen in the solvent seems to produce abnormally high solubilities.

The relative solvent powers of aniline, o-toluidine and pyridine seem to depend, as might be expected, upon their relative strengths as bases. The dissociation constants of these bases in water may be used to indicate their relative powers of attracting CO_2 molecules. Table 8 gives the values found in the literature, together with those for two xylidines.

Although the constant for toluidine is given as practically identical

TABLE 8.

Bases	Dissociation Constants	Temp.	$10^4 N$ for CO_2 at 20°
Aniline	3.2×10^{-10}	15°	55
o-Toluidine	2.9×10^{-10}	15°	66
1-3-4 Xylidine	6.3×10^{-10}	15°	..
1-2-4 Xylidine	9.6×10^{-10}	20°	..
Pyridine	16.0×10^{-10}	18°	129

with that for aniline, the distinctly higher constants for the xylidines indicate that the basic character increases in the order given, which accords fully with the solvent powers for CO_2 repeated in the last column.

Although the solvent power of water for CO_2 is small, despite its tendency to react with CO_2, its solvent power must be regarded as abnormally high on this very account, as comparison with the following ratios for other gases will show.

TABLE 9.

	H_2	N_2	CO	O_2	CO_2
$\dfrac{\text{Solubility in } H_2O}{\text{Solubility in } C_6H_6}$	0.058	0.032	0.031	0.031	0.077
$\dfrac{\text{Solubility in } H_2O}{\text{Solubility in } CS_2}$	....	0.10	0.095	....	0.32

The chemical nature of N_2O is less familiar than that of CO_2, and the data available are less abundant, but its solubilities seem to follow rather closely from the assumption that it is similar to CO_2, but slightly less polar. It is, accordingly, somewhat less soluble than CO_2 in the more polar solvents, but distinctly more soluble in the non-polar solvents, both by reason of its smaller polarity and the larger value for the ideal solubility.[23]

SOLUBILITY OF GASES IN SOLIDS.

The considerations we have previously employed lend themselves to some very interesting extensions relating to the solubility of gases in solids. For example, a very important military problem is the permeability of various balloon fabrics to hydrogen and helium. It is known that fabrics impregnated with cellulose nitrates are much less permeable than those coated with rubber. If we were considering the solubility of hydrogen in isoprene as compared with some

[23] Kunerth has used his own data and those of Just as a basis for a denial of any connection between solubility and internal pressure for gases. He has, however, neglected to make the distinction previously insisted upon by the present author between liquids of low and high polarity. The reader can see that if the more polar liquids are omitted from Table 6 the others fall in the same order, within the limits to be expected, as was found in Table 1 and also throughout this volume for a variety of solubilities and other properties. Cf. Hildebrand, *Phys. Rev.*, **20**, 52 (1923).

liquid ester of nitric acid, we would not hesitate to predict smaller solubility in the latter on account of its greater polarity. It is but a step to the comparison of the solid films first mentioned, in the same way. Indeed, there can hardly be any doubt that the solid film of rubber would show a much smaller dielectric constant than one of cellulose nitrate.

On the other hand, if we were comparing the permeability of these fabrics for some more polar gas, such as NH_3 or SO_2, we would probably not find the cellulose nitrate so resistant.

Similar considerations may be applied to explain the fact, discovered during the war, that cloth carrying a film of solidified linseed oil is far more resistant to "mustard gas" than rubberized fabric. Mustard gas, having a rather low polarity, would doubtless be resisted better by the more polar the film. The dielectric constant might well serve as a rough measure of impermeability.

SOLUBILITIES OF GASES IN AQUEOUS SOLUTIONS.

The solubilities of the inert gases in water are affected in a very regular way by the addition of electrolytes. Most inorganic electrolytes have an effect upon water which may be regarded as increasing the internal pressure. The expression $T(\partial P/\partial T)_v$, or $T\alpha/\beta$, being negative for water below $4°$, is obviously unsuitable as an estimate of this cohesion, and we are forced to more indirect methods of estimation, which, however, agree in their interpretation. The effect of dissolved salts is usually to increase surface tension, decrease compressibility, lower the temperature of maximum density, decrease solvent power for substances of low polarity and internal pressure, and *vice-versa*. Tammann [24] has pointed out that the external pressure has the same effect upon water as does the presence of dissolved electrolytes in altering the expansion, compressibility, temperature of maximum density and temperature of minimum compressibility, and he has proposed to define the increase in the internal pressure of a solution due to the addition of a solute as equal to the external pressure that would have to be applied to pure water in order to make the above properties the same for it as they are for the solution in question. He quotes data to show that these increases in internal pressure, calculated from the different properties, are in good agreement. Since we are more interested in relative than in absolute values it suffices to illustrate by giving the order in which the various solutes affect some of the above properties. Thus the temperature of maximum density of water is lowered as follows for 0.5 molal solutions: NaCl 6.7; KOH 7.3; $CaCl_2$ 10.9; $CuSO_4$ 11.1; H_2SO_4 11.8; K_2CO_3 15.3; K_2SO_4 14.7; Na_2CO_3 15.2; Na_2SO_4 15.6.

[24] Tammann, *Z. physik. Chem.*, 11, 676 (1893), and a series of papers during the following two years. See also monograph "Ueber die Beziehungen zwischen den Inneren Kräften und Eigenschaften der Lösungen." Voss, Leipzig, 1907.

TABLE 10.

RELATIVE COMPRESSIBILITIES OF AQUEOUS SOLUTIONS.

	H	NH$_4$	K	Li	Na
I	....	0.960	0.913	0.918	0.892
NO$_3$	0.980	0.953	0.901	0.893	0.878
Br	0.972	0.953	0.901	0.893	0.878
Cl	0.954	0.933	0.872	0.868	0.849
OH	1.000	1.009	0.779	0.782	0.761
SO$_4$	0.942	0.808	....	0.682	....
CO$_3$	....	....	0.669	0.660	0.644

Watson [25] has discussed the compressibility of aqueous solutions from the standpoint of Tammann, and it is of interest to quote a table which he gives of relative molal compressibilities.

It will be seen that the compressibility diminishes, and therefore the internal pressure increases with the cations in the order H, NH$_4$, K, Li, Na, while the corresponding order for the anions is I, NO$_3$, Br, Cl, OH, SO$_4$, CO$_3$. This agrees well with the relative lowering of the temperature of maximum density given above.

Euler,[26] and later Geffeken,[27] connected this increase in internal pressure brought about by electrolytes with their power to diminish the solubility of gases and certain rather non-polar electrolytes. Table 7 is quoted from the former to show the percent diminution in solubility over that in pure water in the various solutions mentioned.

Allowing for the fact that in this table the solutions are normal instead of molal, as previously, the correlation between solvent power and internal pressure is seen to be good. Similar results are given by Geffeken. We therefore have in such tables relative internal pres-

TABLE 11.

PERCENT DECREASE IN SOLUBILITY IN NORMAL SOLUTIONS OF ELECTROLYTES.

	H$_2$	N$_2$O	N$_2$	CO$_2$	H$_2$S	EtOAc	Et$_2$O
NH$_4$NO$_3$ ...	..	..	..	3	1	..	..
KI	..	..	..	..	2	..	26
KBr	..	..	..	..	6	..	..
KNO$_3$	..	..	..	9	9	12	31
NaNO$_3$	..	..	..	10	11	..	..
LiCl	16	21	..	17	..	..	34
KCl	20	22	..	..	15	30	40
½BaCl$_2$	..	..	32	..	..	..	..
½CaCl$_2$	21	24	..	..	..	..	..
NaCl	22	24	34	..	..	..	..
½(NH$_4$)$_2$SO$_4$.	..	..	..	..	18	..	..
½MgSO$_4$	23	29	..	30	..	39	..
½ZnSO$_4$	23	..	..	30	..	39	..
½K$_2$SO$_4$	..	..	..	..	22	..	..
½Na$_2$SO$_4$	27	30	..	32	27	44	53
½Na$_2$CO$_3$	29	..	..	..	..	..	54
NaOH	..	..	..	..	..	..	54

[25] Watson, *Proc. Roy. Soc., Edin.,* **33**, 282 (1913).
[26] Euler, *Z. physik. Chem.,* **31**, 368 (1898).
[27] Geffeken, *ibid.,* **49**, 287 (1904).

sures or solubility series which should prove of value in estimating the "salting out" powers of electrolytes, and for other substances as well.

It has been shown by Whatmough [28] that the effect of changing composition of a solution is to cause the surface tension and the compressibility to vary in opposite directions. This is, of course, in harmony with the idea that both of these properties are governed by the attractive forces within the solution. When both components are non-polar and of different internal pressure, or one polar and the other non-polar, and when they expand on mixing, we would expect the solution to show a surface tension somewhat less than additive and a compressibility somewhat greater, while with two polar liquids which contract on mixing and evolve heat, as is usually the case, we may look for the opposite effect. Moreover, the foregoing paragraphs indicate that the solvent power of the mixture for other substances should be affected accordingly. The investigations of Christoff [29] and of Ritzel [30] have shown this to be the case. The solubilities of various gases, for example, in mixtures of water and sulfuric acid undergo a pronounced minimum at about 50 percent by weight, while the surface tension undergoes a maximum at this same composition.

[28] Whatmough, *Z. physik. Chem.*, **39**, 129 (1901).
[29] Christoff, *Z. physik. Chem.*, **55**, 630 (1906).
[30] Ritzel, *ibid.*, **60**, 319 (1907).

Chapter XIII.

Solubilities of Liquids in Liquids.

In Chapter V it was shown how positive deviations from Raoult's law, if sufficiently large, are accompanied by separation into two liquid phases. If both liquids are of low polarity the difference in internal pressure must be very large in order for this to occur, the phenomenon occurring only with the liquids at the extremes of the various tables given in Chapter IX as the following cases will show.

The critical mixing temperatures of liquid phosphorus with various liquids were investigated by Buehrer [1] in the author's laboratory with the following results:

TABLE 1.

CRITICAL MIXING TEMPERATURES OF WHITE PHOSPHORUS.

Decane	> 390°	Ethylene bromide	165°
Chlorobenzene	264°	p-Dibromobenzene	163°
Naphthalene	202°	Carbon disulfide	— 6.5°
Phenanthrene	200°	Bromoform	< 0°
Anthracene	~ 198°		

Comparison of the order shown in this table with the relative internal pressures shows substantial agreement. It should be borne in mind that at the temperatures here concerned the relative internal pressures may not be quite the same as at 20°, hence the slight reversal of the order with p-dibromobenzene and ethylene bromide is not very serious. The considerable difference between the critical mixing temperature with carbon disulfide and with ethylene bromide does not altogether harmonize with the much smaller difference in internal pressure or with their more nearly equal solvent powers for many other solutes.

Aniline and hexane [2] furnish another example of partial miscibility without very great polarity in either component. Aniline appears to be nearly normal (VIII) although this may be due to the small effect the amino group is able to exert upon the larger phenyl group. The internal pressure, both from the criteria used in Chapter IX and from the solvent power for gases (Table XII-1) is a little greater than that of carbon disulfide. This, together with its slight polarity is in accord with its ability to form two liquid phases with a liquid of low internal pressure and very low polarity such as hexane. The

---

[1] Hildebrand and Buehrer, *J. Am. Chem. Soc.*, **42**, 2213 (1920).
[2] Hildebrand and Keyes, *J. Am. Chem. Soc.*, **39**, 2126 (1917).

critical mixing temperature was found to be 59.6°. Other properties of this mixture are reported in this paper and their theoretical significance discussed.

Nitrobenzene has a much higher dielectric constant than aniline, but apparently this should not be interpreted as indicating greater polarity, for not only do the criteria for internal pressure yield a somewhat smaller value than for aniline but the solvent power for the non-polar gases (Table XII-1) and for p-dibromobenzene (Table XIV-2) is distinctly greater. In harmony with these facts we find that hexane mixes with nitrobenzene more easily than with aniline, giving a critical temperature of 21.0° as compared with 59.6°. From this we may also conclude that nitrobenzene is less soluble in water than is aniline.

Chloroform is one of those substances referred to in Chapter VIII which has enough polarity to make it distinctly more soluble in polar liquids but not enough to interfere with its ability to mix freely with non-polar substances. Hence its solubility in water is much greater than that of benzene, 0.815 percent by weight as against 0.072 percent for the latter; while its solvent power for the non-polar gases, oxygen, nitrogen and carbon monoxide is almost the same (XII).

Other instances are given in Table 2 showing, for similar substances, the relation between polarity, as indicated by dielectric constant and solubility in water. The figures for solubility have not been recalculated into mol fractions, since the relative values are sufficiently indicated by the original values in weight percent.

TABLE 2.

SOLUBILITIES IN WATER.

Liquid	Dielec. Const.	Solubility wt. percent	t	Crit. Temp.
{ Phenol	9.7	8.40	20°	68.8°
{ Aniline	7.3	3.1	22°	167°
{ Ethyl bromide	9.4	0.905	20°	....
{ Ethyl iodide	7.4	0.401	20°	....
{ Ethyl formate	9.1	10.0	22°	....
{ Ethyl acetate	6.0	~8.0	22°	....
{ Ethyl propionate	5.6	1.7	22°	....

Methyl alcohol is sufficiently polar to give, like water, two liquid phases when mixed with liquids of sufficiently low polarity, although its ability to mix with such liquids is naturally greater than that of water. Examples are methyl alcohol-hexane, critical temperature, 42.8°; and methyl alcohol-carbon disulfide, 40.5°.

There are a few cases in which the mutual solubility of two liquids increases as the temperature is lowered, yielding a lower critical temperature. This occurs with triethylamine and water, 18.6°; collidine and water, 5.7°; and nicotine and water, 60°. (The last named system also shows an upper critical temperature at 210°.) Such a behavior may be connected with the tendency of the less polar component to become more polar as the temperature is lowered—the usual effect of temperature upon polarity—thus increasing its ability to mix with the more polar component. This is not very different from saying that lowering the temperature increases the tendency—where such exists—for the components to combine with each other. The chemical nature of the substances mentioned above indicates a tendency to hydrate which, it is not surprising to find, can counteract the tendency to unmix caused by their otherwise dissimilar nature to water.

Molten sulfur shows a very interesting behavior in that it shows first an upper critical mixing temperature, and also a higher critical unmixing temperature. That is, it is miscible in all proportions with certain liquids within a certain interval but it separates into two liquid phases both at higher and lower temperatures as Table 3 shows.

TABLE 3.

SOLUBILITIES OF MOLTEN SULFUR.

	Critical Temperatures	
	Of mixing	Of unmixing
Paraffin[3]	not reached	....
Xylene[3]	" "	....
Ethyl benzene[3]	190°	....
Toluene[3, 4]	180°	222°
Benzene[3, 4]	163°	226°
Triphenylmethane[5]	147°	199°
β-Dichloroethyl sulfide[6]	143°	....
Aniline[4]	138°	....
Benzyl chloride[7]	134°	....
Chlorobenzene[4]	116°	....
Naphthalene[3] ⎫		
Diphenyl[3] ⎪		
Phenanthrene[3] ⎬	miscible	....
p-Dibromobenzene[3] ⎪		
Methylene iodide ⎭		

The order in Table 3 is the familar internal pressure series for the substances of low polarity. For aniline and β-dichloroethyl sulfide ("mustard gas") the critical temperatures are higher than their relatively high internal pressures would indicate, on account, doubtless, of the moderate polarity of these liquids, sulfur having a high internal pressure but very low polarity. The unmixing at a higher temperature may be attributed to the change from S_λ to S_μ which takes place gradually in this region and which so profoundly alters

[3] Kruyt, *Z. physik. Chem.*, **64**, 486 (1909).
[4] Alexejeff, *Wied. Ann.*, **28**, 305 (1886).
[5] Smith, Holmes and Hall, *Z. physik. Chem.*, **52**, 602 (1905).
[6] Wilkinson, Neilson and Wylde, *J. Am. Chem. Soc.*, **42**, 1377 (1920).
[7] Boguski and Jakubowski, *J. Russ. Phys. Ges.*, **37**, 92 (1905); *Chem. Zentr.* (1905), I, 1207.

the nature of the sulfur as nearly to produce two liquid phases with the pure element, S_μ being evidently a substance of very different internal pressure from S_λ.

The relation between dielectric constant and solubility in water was pointed out by Rothmund,[8] who gave the following solubility series: water, lower fatty acids, lower alcohols, lower ketones, lower aldehydes, nitriles, phenols, aromatic aldehydes, ether, halogenated hydrocarbons, carbon disulfide, aromatic hydrocarbons, saturated aliphatic hydrocarbons. Walden[9] pointed out the approximate parallelism between the dielectric constant and the values for internal pressure which he obtained, and concluded as follows: "It is possible therefore to announce as a qualitative rule for the relative solubilities of various liquids in water, that the solubility parallels the internal pressure; the smaller the difference in the internal pressures of two media the greater is their mutual solubility, while solvents whose internal pressures differ widely are only slightly soluble in each other (for example, water and the hydrocarbons). However, it should not be claimed that other factors besides internal pressures (for example capillary influences between the two media), do not also influence the mutual solubility."

This is probably the first statement of the internal pressure theory of solubility. It should be pointed out, however, that as above stated it may lead to error, for it is necessary to have regard not only to the magnitude of the field of force surrounding a molecule but also to the symmetry or polarity of the field. Thus, although the methods for determining internal pressure indicate that the polar substances have abnormally high internal pressures, we find a great difference between the solubilities in water of liquid phosphorus or sulfur, on the one hand, and acetic acid or glycerine on the other. In fact, the solubility of a liquid in water is governed chiefly by its polarity, so that the generalization of Rothmund is much nearer the truth, so far as water is concerned, than that of Walden. It is only when substances of low polarity are considered that the latter's statement is true. We may also reiterate here the importance of a rational method of expressing solubilities, the lack of which has introduced contradictions into much of the work upon solubility.

The effect of a second solute upon the solubility of the first is predictable upon the basis of the principles used in the preceding chapter to account for similar effects upon the solubilities of gases. Thus the solvent power of water for a non-polar substance is usually decreased by the addition of a salt, the relative "salting out" powers following the same series as for gases. Again, the addition of a liquid of intermediate polarity, such as alcohol, increases the miscibility of a polar liquid, such as water, with a non-polar liquid, such as hexane. Many examples might be given were it necessary to do so.[10]

[8] Rothmund, *Z. physik. Chem.*, **26**, 489 (1898).
[9] Walden, *ibid.*, **66**, 409 (1909).
[10] Cf. Timmermans, *Z. physik. Chem.*, **58**, 129 (1907).

Effect of Pressure Upon the Miscibility of Liquids.

The condition for equilibrium between two liquid phases as pressure is changed is that the fugacity of each component shall remain the same in the two phases. This can be expressed by the equation

$$\frac{d \ln f_1}{d P} = \frac{d \ln f_1'}{d P},\qquad (1)$$

where f_1 denotes the fugacity of X_1 in the phase rich in X_1 and f_1' its fugacity in the phase poor in X_1. Now, in changing the pressure, the composition of both phases is altered, so that we can write

$$\frac{d \ln f_1}{d P} = \left(\frac{\partial \ln f_1}{\partial \ln N_1}\right)_P \frac{\partial \ln N_1}{d P} + \left(\frac{\partial \ln f_1}{\partial P}\right)_N,\qquad (2)$$

and an identical equation for f_1'. Substituting these values in Equation 1 above gives

$$\left(\frac{\partial \ln f_1}{\partial \ln N_1}\right)_P \frac{d \ln N_1}{d P} + \left(\frac{\partial \ln f_1}{\partial P}\right)_N =$$

$$\left(\frac{\partial \ln f_1'}{\partial \ln N_1'}\right)_P \frac{d \ln N_1'}{d P} + \left(\frac{\partial \ln f_1'}{\partial P}\right)_N,$$

and substituting

$$\left(\frac{\partial \ln f_1}{\partial P}\right)_N = \frac{\overline{v}_1}{RT}, \quad \text{and} \left(\frac{\partial \ln f_1'}{\partial P}\right)_N = \frac{\overline{v}_1'}{RT},$$

(Equation VI-7), gives

$$\left(\frac{\partial \ln f_1}{\partial \ln N_1}\right)_P \frac{d \ln N_1}{d P} + \frac{\overline{v}_1}{RT} = \left(\frac{\partial \ln f_1'}{\partial \ln N_1'}\right)_P \frac{d \ln N_1'}{d P} + \frac{\overline{v}_1'}{RT}\qquad (3)$$

This is an exact equation to which any two-phase liquid system must conform.

We may make an approximate application of this equation to a type of system which occurs frequently, in which the solubility curve is fairly symmetrical and where the partial molal volume of each component increases upon dilution (corresponding to expansion upon mixing the pure liquids, cf. p. 61). In such a case

$$\left(\frac{\partial \ln f_1}{\partial \ln N_1}\right)_P = \left(\frac{\partial \ln f_1'}{\partial \ln N_1'}\right)_P,$$

since by the Duhem Equation

$$\frac{\partial \ln f_1}{\partial \ln N_1} = \frac{\partial \ln f_2}{\partial \ln N_2},$$

13

and for a symmetrical system

$$\frac{\partial \ln f_2}{\partial \ln N_2} = \frac{\partial \ln f_1'}{\partial \ln N_1'}.$$

Equation 3 therefore becomes

$$\left(\frac{\partial \ln f_1}{\partial \ln N_1}\right)_P \cdot \frac{d \ln \frac{N_1}{N_1'}}{d P} = \frac{\overline{v_1}' - \overline{v_1}}{RT}. \tag{4}$$

Since the primed numbers have been taken to represent the phase poor in X_1, $N_1 > N_1'$ and $\overline{v_1}' > \overline{v_1}$. Therefore the right hand member of Equation 4 is positive, and since $\left(\dfrac{\partial \ln f_1}{\partial \ln N_1}\right)$ is positive, $\dfrac{d \ln \frac{N_1}{N_1'}}{dP}$ is positive, and N_1/N_1' becomes larger with increasing pressure, and the mutual solubility of the liquids becomes smaller.

Exceptions to this general conclusion, which will doubtless be found in harmony with the behavior of most two-phase liquid mixtures, may, of course, arise when either the fugacity or the partial molal volume varies in a more unusual way. An extended and important study of the effect of pressure upon liquid miscibility has been made by Timmermans.[11]

[11] Timmermans, Thesis, Brussels, 1911. *Bull. Soc. chim. Bel.*, **30**, 276 (1921).

Chapter XIV.

Solubilities of Solid Non-Electrolytes.

The basis for calculating the ideal solubility of a solid, assuming Raoult's law, has been set forth in Chapter IV, and it is the purpose of the present chapter to discuss the deviations from the ideal solubility caused by the other factors involved. Most of the solubility data available have to do with salts in water, and to a lesser degree in other polar solvents such as the alcohols and acetone. But few experimenters have busied themselves with the solubilities of relatively non-polar solids in liquids of the same type, where the behavior is most easily recognized as regular. We will give first data for several of the simplest cases, and proceed later to take up some of the more complex.

IODINE.

The solubilities of iodine furnish a particularly suitable illustration of the various aspects of the theory because the colors of the solution serve to indicate those in which solvation occurs, and therefore to supplement in an altogether independent way the evidence furnished by the solubility curves themselves. Since liquid iodine may be regarded as a rather non-polar substance of high internal pressure, occurring at the bottom of several of the internal pressure tables in Chapter IX, we may expect that its solubility will fall off as we ascend to the solvents higher up in the table, whose internal pressures are lower. Polar solvents introduce uncertainties, due especially to the possibility of solvation and consequent increases in solubility over what would otherwise be the case. Now ordinarily we find it difficult to predict when such solvation will occur, so that our solubility predictions are correspondingly uncertain, but with iodine solvation seems to be accompanied by a change in color from violet to yellow or brown.[1] The violet solutions, therefore, are those whose solubilities should accord with the internal pressure series, while the solubilities in the yellow or brown solutions should be abnormally high.

Fig. 1 represents most of the reliable solubility data to be found for this solute, plotted after the manner described in Chapter IV, log N_2 against $1/T$. The data plotted were obtained from the follow-

---

[1] Hildebrand and Glascock, *J. Am. Chem. Soc.*, **31**, 26 (1909). See also P. Waentig, *Z. physik. Chem.*, **68**, 513 (1909), and Hildebrand, *ibid.*, **74**, 679 (1910).

ing sources: solubilities in benzene, carbon tetrachloride and heptane, Hildebrand and Jenks;[2] in benzene and in carbon disulfide by Arctowski;[3] in chloroform and in glycerine by Hantzsch and Vagt;[4] in carbon tetrachloride and in bromoform by Jakowkin;[5] in molten sulfur by Smith and Carson.[6] Table 1 gives the smoothed out values

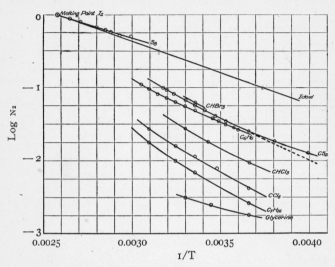

FIG. 1.—Solubilities of Iodine.

got from Fig. 1 for the solvents that have been measured over a sufficient range of temperature to justify this procedure.

The ideal solubility is calculated by the aid of the value of Lewis and Randall for the free energy change from liquid to solid iodine, —920 cals. per mol, which is Δ_F (liq. to solid) $= RT \ln f^s/f^o$. But

TABLE 1.

SOLUBILITIES OF IODINE—MOL PERCENT.

Solvent	0°	10°	20°	25°	40°	50°
Glycerine	0.189	0.215	0.256	0.282	...	...
Heptane	0.245	0.376	0.565	0.679	1.19	1.70
Carbon tetrachloride	0.418	0.631	0.920	1.10	1.69	2.68
Chloroform	0.93	1.35	1.93	2.28	(3.80)	(5.30)
Benzene	...	3.06	4.20	4.82	7.18	9.50
Carbon disulfide	2.50	3.41	4.87	5.70	9.25	12.7
Bromoform	...	(3.9)	(5.31)	6.16	(10.5)	...
Ideal	18.4	19.6	20.6	21.2	22.9	24.0

[2] Hildebrand and Jenks, *J. Am. Chem. Soc.*, **42**, 2180 (1920).
[3] Arctowski, *Z. Anorg. Chem.*, **6**, 404 (1894).
[4] Hantzsch and Vagt, *Z. physik. Chem.*, **38**, 728 (1901).
[5] Jakowkin, *ibid.*, **18**, 590 (1895).
[6] Smith and Carson, *ibid.*, **61**, 200 (1907).

since the fugacity of solid iodine is equal to the fugacity of iodine in the saturated solution, we may substitute N for f^s/f°, for the ideal solution, getting $-920 = 4.58 \times 298 \log N$, and $\log N = \bar{1}.327$ at 25°. (Cf. Equation III-18.)

It is evident from Fig. 1 that the curves for carbon bisulfide, chloroform, carbon tetrachloride and heptane form a family in which the deviation from the ideal is in the order to be expected from internal pressures. The color of these solutions moreover, indicates that the iodine is little affected by the solvent, so that internal pressure and not solvation should largely determine the course of the curves.

The solvents which give brown solutions, on the other hand, behave very differently. Glycerine is rather strongly polar and is a poor solvent in spite of the high degree of solvation, as indicated both by the brown color of the solution and by the fact that as the temperature increases the solubility increases far less rapidly than it would for a violet solution, indicating an approach to its normal position as the solvation diminishes with the temperature. (Cf. p. 58.) It is evidently a better solvent than it would be in the absence of solvation.

The case of benzene is similar though much less pronounced. The solution has a brownish red color which approaches violet when heated and becomes browner when cooled. The solubility in benzene is therefore much greater than in chloroform, whose internal pressure is almost the same, but as the solvation diminishes with rising temperature the curve for chloroform is approached. If these solutions were not colored this explanation might seem less convincing, and we will find later many examples of deviation from the simple family of curves that cannot at present be predicted with any great degree of certainty. Who, for example, would dare predict that iodine will form a solvate with benzene but not with chloroform, which is equally polar, while acetone and ether form solvates with chloroform but not with benzene? The abnormal slope of the solubility curve makes the existence of the solvation evident, but this is explaining solubility curves rather than predicting them.

A similar behavior is shown by carbon disulfide solutions below 0°, when they begin to turn brown, indicating solvation, and higher solubilities than would be the case if the solutions remained violet. The dotted lower extension shows the approximate course the curve would undoubtedly take if solvation were absent. It should be noted that any estimate of the degree of solvation should be based upon the deviation from this dotted curve rather than from the line for the ideal solution higher up. The well-nigh universal practice of concluding that all deviations from Raoult's law (or, still worse, from van't Hoff's law for osmotic pressure, or from any of the laws derived therefrom) indicate changes in the molecular species present in the solution is far from being justifiable, as these curves clearly show. The considerable deviations which would be found in the molecular weight of iodine dissolved in heptane might be "explained" by assuming that iodine is "associated" in heptane, or, if preferred, that heptane is associated. However, there is obviously no more reason for such assumptions with heptane than there is with carbon disulfide. All of the violet solutions should be regarded as ideal in the sense that chemical effects, or changes in the molecular species, are absent. We may have considerable confidence, accordingly, that the line drawn to represent the solubility in bromoform would be closely substantiated by experiment, in spite of the fact that we have but a single measurement. Indeed, the fact that bromoform has a higher internal pressure than carbon disulfide would serve to fix the position of this curve within a very narrow region. Ethylene bromide, which also gives a violet solution, has an internal pressure somewhat less than carbon bisulfide, so that its solvent power for iodine may be predicted by drawing a curve a little below and parallel to the curve for carbon disulfide.

The solvent power of ethyl acetate, which gives a brown solution, approaching violet at higher temperatures, is far more difficult to predict. Its internal pressure is between those of heptane and carbon tetrachloride, and if it dissolved iodine with a violet color the solubility curve would doubtless fall between the curves for these solvents. The solvation which the color indicates, however, would operate to produce a deviation, increasing as the temperature is lowered, in the direction of greater solubility, making the curve much flatter than it would be if the solution were violet.

It is evident that in the absence of color we could not be nearly as confident regarding the solvents whose curves would fall in with the parallel family governed by internal pressure, but that our predictions made upon this basis would more often be found incorrect due to solvation such as shown by iodine and benzene or ether, and which the present state of our knowledge of chemistry does not suffice to predict. The following sections will contain frequent surprises of this sort, increasing as the more polar substances are examined.

SULFUR.

The solubilities of sulfur have been the subject of frequent investigation. We have data by Etard[7] for hexane, benzene, ethylene bromide and carbon bisulfide; by Gerardin[8] for stannic chloride in the neighborhood of the melting point of sulfur; by Aten[9] for sulfur monochloride; by Smith and Carson[10] for iodine; by Cossa[11] for chloroform, ethyl ether, benzene, carbon disulfide and toluene; by Retgers[12] for methylene iodide; by Brönsted[13] for benzene, iodo-

[7] Etard, *Ann. chim. phys.*, **2**, 571 (1894).
[8] Gerardin, *ibid.*, **5**, 129 (1865).
[9] Aten, *Z. physik. Chem.*, **54**, 86, 124 (1905).
[10] Smith and Carson, *ibid.*, **61**, 200 (1909).
[11] Cossa, *Ber.*, **1**, 38 (1868).
[12] Retgers, *Z. anorg. Chem.*, **3**, 347 (1893).
[13] Brönsted, *Z. physik. Chem.*, **55**, 371 (1906).

benzene and chloroform; by Hoffman [14] for carbon tetrachloride, dichloro-ethylene, ethylene chloride, pentachloro-ethane, perchloro-ethylene, trichloro-ethylene and tetrachloro-ethane. There are other data for more or less polar solvents, including phenol,[15] naphthol,[15] alcohols,[16] and ammonia.[17]

Some of the data referred to are obviously not very accurate, and many of the determinations were made only at one temperature. Accordingly it has been desirable to check certain portions and to supple-

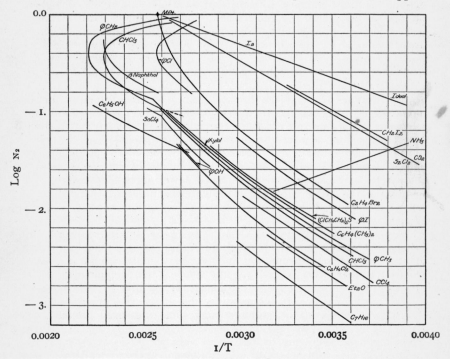

FIG. 2.—Solubilities of Sulfur.

ment others, and Hildebrand and Jenks [18] have measured solubilities in carbon tetrachloride, benzene, toluene, m-xylene, heptane and ethylene chloride.

It seems unnecessary to take up the space that would be necessary for the tabulation of this mass of data, as our purpose is better served by its graphic representation in Fig. 2. The line corresponding to the ideal solubility is calculated from the melting point and the

[14] Hoffman, *Ber.*, **43**, 188 (1910).
[15] Smith, Holmes and Hall, *J. Am. Chem. Soc.*, **27**, 805 (1905).
[16] De Bruyn, *Z. physik. Chem.*, **10**, 781 (1892).
[17] Ruff and Hecht, *Z. anorg. Chem.*, **70**, 61 (1911).
[18] Hildebrand and Jenks, *J. Am. Chem. Soc.*, **43**, 2172 (1921).

heat of fusion of rhombic sulfur, using data given in a paper by Lewis and Randall,[19] and corresponds to an ideal solubility for S_8 of mol fraction 0.282 at 25°. The heat of solution of sulfur in such a solvent is the same as its heat of fusion, or, in other words, such a solvent would mix with molten sulfur with no heat effect.

The relatively high internal pressure of sulfur, close to that of iodine, is indicated by the following data. Toepler[20] has given the specific volume of supercooled sulfur at 20° as 0.951 times the specific volume at 120°, which according to Pisati[21] is 0.5541. From these figures we calculate the molecular volume of liquid sulfur S_8, at 20° as 135 cc. The surface tension of sulfur at 20° is 60.0.[22] This gives $\gamma/v^{1/3} = 11.7$, which would place sulfur close to iodine in internal pressure.

From the vapor pressure measurements of Ruff and Graf[23] we calculate the heat of vaporization of sulfur at low temperatures to be 19,100 cals. per mol. From this we get $(L - RT)/v = 137$, which, again, would place sulfur just above iodine in internal pressure. Unfortunately, data do not exist for the calculation of the internal pressure by the more accurate method of our sixth paper.

We should thus expect that sulfur would obey Raoult's law rather closely with iodine, and that its solubility would decrease progressively as we change to solvents of lower internal pressure. By comparing the order of the curves with the order of internal pressures given in Chapter IX it will be seen that on the whole the agreement is very good.

A minor discrepancy exists in the cases of benzene, toluene, and xylene. The last named has an internal pressure about the same as that of carbon tetrachloride, and usually exhibits the same solvent power, so that order found for the above three homologues is the reverse of the order expected. This may be due to the influence of the partial molal volumes as suggested at the end of Chapter VI. Mr. C. A. Jenks, at the author's suggestion, measured the densities of dilute solutions of sulfur in these three solvents and calculated from them the following partial molal volumes of S_8 at 25°: in benzene, 138.7 cc.; toluene, 133.4 cc.; m-xylene, 123.6 cc. These figures may be interpreted as indicating that the packing of sulfur molecules among those of the solvents occurs most readily with xylene and least with benzene, giving rise to the observed order of solubility rather than that usually found.

Ethylene chloride shows an abnormally low solvent power. Its internal pressure is greater than that of benzene, but its solvent power for sulfur is considerably less than that of carbon tetrachloride. This is probably due to its polar character, as shown by its dielectric con-

[19] Lewis and Randall, *J. Am. Chem. Soc.*, **36**, 2468 (1914).
[20] Toepler, *Wied. Ann.*, **47**, 169 (1892).
[21] Pisati, *Gazz. chim. ital.*, **4**, 29 (1874).
[22] Cf. Harkins, Davies and Clark, *J. Am. Chem. Soc.*, **39**, 541 (1917).
[23] Ruff and Graf, *Ber.*, **40**, 4199 (1907).

stant of 10.4. The dielectric constant of liquid sulfur is only 3.4. As the polar character diminishes with rising temperature we find the solvent power of ethylene chloride increasing somewhat more rapidly with temperature than does that of a normal substance such as carbon tetrachloride. Ethylene bromide, with a smaller dielectric constant, 4.9, shows a solvent power nearly as great as its internal pressure would lead one to expect. Tetrachloroethylene, C_2Cl_4, with a dielectric constant of only 2.46, has about the solvent power indicated by its internal pressure. The other solvents investigated by Hoffman have not been included in the plot, partly because of lack of space, partly because of lack of knowledge concerning their physical constants. In general, however, their solvent powers seem to accord well with the theory.

The figures of Aten for sulfur monochloride show, when plotted, considerable irregularity. Those for hexane by Etard, not included in the plot, are very close to our own for heptane, but a smaller slope than that of the other curves of the family as well as considerable irregularity indicates some inaccuracy. The small solubility of sulfur in hexane makes accurate determinations difficult.

The curve for ammonia, which is included as an interesting illustration of a solvent power probably attributable to solvation, falls off with increasing temperature, quite unlike any of the other cases given. The prediction of such behavior awaits a far greater knowledge of the causes of chemical combination than we now possess, although it is interesting to note that the electron structures of the sulfur atom and the ammonia molecule make plausible the formation of a complex having the structure:

$$H:\overset{..}{\underset{H}{N}}:\overset{..}{\underset{..}{S}}:$$

It will be noted that the deviations from Raoult's law for many of the substances represented is sufficient to prevent the solubility curves for solid rhombic sulfur from ending directly at its melting point in complete miscibility. Instead, two liquid phases are formed whose solubility relations and critical mixing temperatures are indicated by loops of the familiar type discussed in the previous chapter. The ease with which sulfur can be supercooled makes possible the investigation of such a system as chlorobenzene-liquid sulfur, shown in the figure, below the melting point of sulfur.

It is of interest in this connection to recall the critical mixing temperatures of sulfur with other liquids given in Table XIII-3.

Naphthalene.

With naphthalene, whose internal pressure places it midway in the tables in Chapter IX, the theory leads us to expect maximum solubility in the adjacent liquids, falling off as the internal pressure of the solvent is either increased or diminished.

The solubilities of naphthalene in benzene, carbon tetrachloride and chlorobenzene were investigated by Schroeder [24] to test the equation he developed connecting the solubility expressed as mol fraction with the heat of fusion of the solute.[25] In addition to these data we have others by Etard [26] for the solvents hexane, carbon disulfide and chloroform. Data by Speyers [27] for chloroform and toluene show

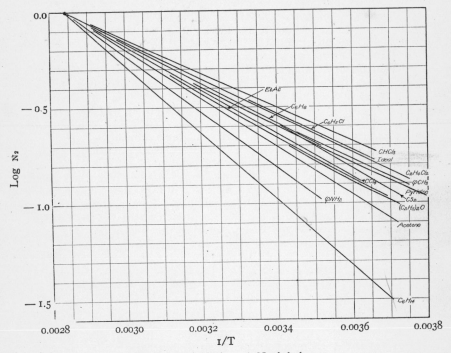

FIG. 3.—Solubilities of Naphthalene.

such fluctuations when plotted as to indicate inferior accuracy, and are omitted from the plot. Data for toluene, ether, aniline, acetone, pyridine, ethylene dichloride and ethyl acetate have been kindly furnished the author by Dr. H. Lee Ward.

Fig. 3 represents the plot of the foregoing data after the usual manner. The ideal solubility has been previously calculated.[28] It will be seen that the solvents of low polarity and below naphthalene

[24] Schroeder, *Z. physik. Chem.*, **11**, 449 (1893).
[25] Equation IV-7.
[26] Etard, *Bull. Soc. chim.* [3], **9**, 82 (1893).
[27] Speyers, *Am. J. Sci.* [4], **14**, 294 (1902).
[28] Page 37.

in internal pressure, show increasing solvent powers in the order hexane, ether, ethyl acetate, carbon tetrachloride, toluene, benzene, chlorobenzene ideal, which is exactly the order of internal pressures. Chloroform, which usually has solvent powers close to those of benzene, is here slightly better than the ideal solvent, indicating possibly a slight unforeseen solvation. Continuing then to solvents of higher internal pressures the order is ethylene chloride, carbon disulfide, aniline, again the expected order, to which we may add lastly molten phosphorus, of very high internal pressure, in which naphthalene is so insoluble as to form two liquid phases up to 202°.[29]

The position of the curves for the highly polar solvents acetone and pyridine is, as usual, difficult to correlate with other information. Naphthalene being rather non-polar, the low solvent power of acetone is less surprising than the higher solvent power of pyridine.

SOLUBILITIES OF p-DIBROMOBENZENE, PHENANTHRENE, TRIPHENYL METHANE, ANTHRACENE AND ANTHRAQUINONE.

These solutes give solubility curves similar to those for naphthalene, so that it suffices to tabulate the data for a single temperature, as shown in Table 2. The internal pressures of the first two of these solvents are given in the tables in Chapter IX as somewhat above carbon disulfide. The maximum solubility should therefore be shown by solvents in this region, falling off as solvents of lower internal pressure are selected, as is indeed the case. Anthracene is so similar

TABLE 2.

SOLUBILITIES IN MOL PERCENT.[32]

Solvent	p-Dibromo-benzene, 25°	Phenan-threne, 25°	Triphenyl-methane, 20°	Anthra-cene, 25°	Anthra-quinone, 25°
Ideal [33]	24.8	22.1	22.9	1.07	0.23
Hexane	8.6	4.2	3.0 [36]	0.18	...
Ether	18.3	15.1	...	0.59	...
Carbon tetrachloride	19.3	18.6	...	0.63	...
Chloroform	...	...	25.8 [36]	...	0.40 [37]
Benzene	21.7	20.7	32.4 [35]	0.81	0.12 [37]
Carbon disulfide	22.4	25.5	19.1 [36]	1.12	...
Nitrobenzene	17.4 [34]	...	...	...	...
Aniline	10.7 [34]	...	...	...	...
Phenol	4.67 [34]	...	...	...	...
Ethyl alcohol	1.98	1.25	...	0.09	0.097

[29] Table XIII-1.
[32] Data by Hildebrand, Ellefson and Beebe, *J. Am. Chem. Soc.*, **39**, 2301 (1917).
[33] Cf. Hildebrand, *J. Am. Chem. Soc.*, **39**, 2297 (1917).
[34] F. S. Mortimer, private communication.
[35] Linebarger, *Am. Chem. J.*, **15**, 46 (1911).
[36] Etard, *Bull. Soc. Chim.* [3], **9**, 82 (1893).
[37] Tyrer, *J. Chem. Soc.*, **97**, 1778 (1910).

to phenanthrene, that the order shown in the table is such as we would expect.

The position of triphenylmethane may be estimated from the following data. Its molecular solution volume in benzene and in chloroform, according to Tyrer,[30] is about 264 cc. at 25°, which we may change to 260 cc. at 20°. From this, together with an extrapolated figure for surface tension,[31] $\gamma = 44.7$ at 20°, the boiling point, 360°, and the van der Waals a (calculated by the method of van Laar) 0.2850, we calculate the following:

$$\gamma/v^{\frac{1}{3}} = 7.1; \quad (5200 + 30\,t_b)/v = 64; \quad a/v^2 = 4.6.$$

These figures do not agree very closely, as we might expect in such a case, as to the relative internal pressure of this substance compared with the substances in the tables in Chapter IX, but they indicate in a general way that it belongs in the same region as benzene. In accordance with this position the solubility both in hexane and in carbon disulfide is less than the ideal. The solubility in benzene on the other hand, is considerably greater than the ideal value, which usually indicates solvation. It is not strange, therefore, to find that this substance is able to crystallize with benzene of crystallization.

Anthraquinone contains the polar carbonyl group, which greatly influences its solubility. It is considerably less soluble in benzene than the ideal value would indicate; it is nearly as soluble in ethyl alcohol as in benzene, and like another ketone, acetone, it evidently tends to solvate with chloroform (p. 42). On account of its polarity it is doubtless relatively more soluble in the other polar solvents at the bottom of the table than is p-dibromobenzene, where the polarity of the solvent is accompanied by a diminution in solvent power.

ALUMINUM BROMIDE.

This is a compound which is sufficiently symmetrical to behave as a relatively non-polar substance towards some solvents. On the other hand its electron structure,

$$\begin{array}{c} : \overset{..}{\text{Br}} : \\[4pt] : \overset{..}{\text{Br}} : \overset{..}{\text{Al}} \\[4pt] : \overset{..}{\text{Br}} : \end{array}$$

shows a pair of electrons lacking about the central atom which can be supplied weakly by a pair on a bromine atom of another molecule, causing polymerization, higher freezing point, due to the orienting force, and especially great tendency to combine with water and other oxygen compounds, as well as with other halogen compounds, as illustrated by the Friedel and Crafts reaction. (Cf. p. 121.)

[30] Tyrer, *J. Chem. Soc.*, **97**, 2620 (1910).
[31] Harkins, Davies and Clark, *J. Am. Chem. Soc.*, **39**, 555 (1917).

When this tendency to form addition compounds is absent it may be expected to behave as a normal substance of rather high internal pressure, like bromine, bromoform, etc. Data by Menschutkin [38] are in harmony with this view. Solubilities at 20° in mol percent are as follows: p-xylene, 18.08; toluene, 18.15; benzene, 20.27; ethylene bromide, 33.9. The molal heat of fusion, 2790 cals.,[39] and the melting point, 96°, give as the ideal solubility at 20°, 38 mol percent. From these figures we might predict the solubility in certain other non-polar solvents with some confidence. The work of Menschutkin shows compounds to be formed between $AlBr_3$ and benzoyl chloride, benzophenone, nitrobenzene, the chloronitrobenzenes, bromonitrobenzenes and nitrotoluenes. The formation of these compounds, of course, increases the solubility of the aluminum bromide far beyond the ideal value.

BENZOIC ACID.

This acid may serve to illustrate a substance whose molecule is non-polar in one part and polar in another, the phenyl and the carboxyl radicals respectively. Its solubilities in various solvents according to Seidell [40] are shown in Table 3, together with the ideal value calculated from the melting point, 121°, and the heat of fusion, 19.2 cals.[41]

TABLE 3.
SOLUBILITIES OF BENZOIC ACID AT 25°—MOL FRACTION.

Ideal	0.38	Chloroform	0.149
Ether	0.347	Carbon disulfide	0.0302
Xylene	0.0856	Ethyl alcohol	0.346
Toluene	0.0828	Nitrobenzene	0.1012
Carbon tetrachloride	0.0518	Water	0.00055
Benzene	0.0816		

We see from this table that the ideal solubility is practically reached in ether and ethyl alcohol, both of which have a polar and a non-polar part, like the benzoic acid. Nitrobenzene, which fulfills the same condition to a lesser degree, is a better solvent than benzene and its non-polar homologues. We note further the low solubility in the non-polar carbon tetrachloride and carbon disulfide, whereas chloroform, much more polar, and which we have elsewhere found to form complexes with ether-oxygen and carboxyl-oxygen, is a much better solvent. Water is too highly polar to allow easy penetration by the phenyl group, so that it is a very poor solvent. We might expect to find that methyl alcohol would be much better, though inferior to ethyl alcohol, and further that the solubility would again fall off in the

[38] Cf. Seidell, "Solubilities of Inorganic and Organic Compounds" (1919), p. 21.

[39] Kablukow, *Centr.* (1908), II, 486.

[40] Seidell, *Bull. U. S. Pub. Health Ser.*, No. 67 (1910).

[41] Hess, *Wied. Ann.*, 35, 425 (1888).

higher alcohols, which contain too much non-polar portion in their molecules.

Various other predictions might be hazarded, such as the following. Bromoform, less polar than chloroform and having a higher internal pressure should be a poorer solvent than the latter. Ethylene bromide, less polar, should be still poorer, probably a little better than a carbon disulfide. Aniline, slightly polar and basic, should be a better solvent than nitrobenzene. Hexane, non-polar, and of very low internal pressure, should be a very poor solvent.

The foregoing examples may suffice to illustrate, first, the considerable degree of confidence with which we can predict the approximate solubility relations of substances of low polarity, and second, the greater uncertainties that are introduced by polar substances, and the nature of the considerations that may be invoked in such cases.

SOLUBILITY CALCULATIONS BY THE METHOD OF MORTIMER.

The calculations outlined in Chapter IX may be given here in Table 4, to illustrate their applicability.

For the substances of low polarity the agreement is very satisfactory. Where one or both substances are polar it is naturally much less close, although even here it is evidently of value.

Where many calculations are desired the graphic method of finding the factors in Equation IX-17, described in the first paper of Mortimer's, will be found convenient. When the heat of fusion is not known, it can be estimated from the slope of a solubility curve by the aid of Table IX-9.

TABLE 4.

Solvent	Solute	Solubility at 20° Observed	Calculated
Benzene	p-Dibromobenzene	0.202	0.202
Toluene	"	0.197	0.200
Carbon tetrachloride	"	0.159	0.163
Nitrobenzene	"	0.144	0.148
Aniline	"	0.085	0.085
Phenol (40°)	"	0.017	0.151
Ethyl alcohol	"	0.028	0.008
" "	Acetanilide	0.212	0.193
Toluene	"	0.004	0.011
Ethyl alcohol	Resorcinol	0.389	0.217
Water	"	0.166	0.149
Acetic acid	"	0.176	0.091
Nitrobenzene	"	0.066	0.040
Chlorobenzene	Fluorene	0.124	0.125
Nitrobenzene	"	0.118	0.126
Benzene	"	0.105	0.109
Carbon tetrachloride	"	0.078	0.084
Acetone	"	0.047	0.076
Aniline	"	0.056	0.058
Ethyl alcohol	"	0.005	0.003
Acetic acid	"	0.008	0.021

The Choice of Solvent for Recrystallization.

This is a matter of such importance that a few words upon the subject may not be amiss. In purifying substances by crystallizing from hot solution it is desirable to use a solvent in which the substance is not very soluble at ordinary temperatures, but in which its solubility increases as rapidly as possible with the temperature. It is well, also, to choose a solvent in which the impurities which may be present will be as soluble as possible at the lower temperatures. When the substance to be purified has a low melting point it will be very soluble in liquids having a similar internal pressure and polarity, hence it is better to select a solvent different from the solute in one or the other of these factors, so as to produce a smaller solubility. This has the additional advantage of giving a larger temperature coefficient of solubility, for Raoult's law is almost invariably approached more closely at higher temperatures than at lower. For example, a paraffin of melting point below 100° would be most soluble (in terms of mol fraction) in liquids like hexane, silicon tetrachloride and mesitylene, and its solubility being already a maximum, so far as the choice of solvent is concerned, would not increase so rapidly with temperature as would its solubility in a liquid like ethylene bromide, its solutions with which would deviate considerably from Raoult's law on account of the difference in internal pressure; or in a liquid like alcohol where the deviation would be due to difference in polarity. Hence, in cooling from, say, 50° to 20°, a greater portion of the paraffin would separate from its solutions in ethylene bromide or alcohol than from a solution in hexane. Moreover, in this case the impurities present would likely be substances of higher internal pressure than the paraffin, such as unsaturated bodies, which would remain in the mother liquor more readily if the solvent were one of higher internal pressure or polarity.

Where a substance of high melting point and low solubility, such as anthracene, is being recrystallized, it may be desirable to use a solvent of similar internal pressure in order to secure larger solubility than would be possible in a liquid of very different internal pressure or of high polarity.

Molecular Weight from Lowering of the Freezing Point.

Before closing the chapter it may not be out of place to utter the same word of caution regarding the use of data upon the lowering of freezing point of the solvent to prove association that was given earlier (p. 129) concerning boiling point data. Thus, we might regard the solubility data for naphthalene in the light of freezing point lowerings of naphthalene brought about by the other components as solutes, and using Equation IV-6, or a simplification of it, calculate the apparent molecular weights of the respective components from the extent to which they lower the freezing point of naphthalene. This would amount to assuming that all of these solutes would give mixtures with naphthalene which would obey Raoult's law, except for association in solution. Thus, we might conclude that hexane is a highly associated liquid when dissolved in naphthalene. The absurdity of such a conclusion is evident, yet the literature is full of similar instances.

EFFECT OF PRESSURE UPON THE SOLUBILITY OF SOLIDS.[42]

When pressure is applied to both the solid and liquid phase of a solution in equilibrium with a solid the composition of the solution is in general altered so as to keep the fugacity of the substance in the solid the same as in the solution, i.e.,

$$\frac{d \ln f^s}{d P} = \frac{d \ln f}{d P}. \tag{1}$$

Now, the change of the fugacity of the solid with pressure is given by the equation

$$\frac{d \ln f^s}{d P} = \frac{v'}{RT}, \tag{2}$$

where v' is the molal volume of the solid. The fugacity of this component of the solution is altered not only by the increased pressure but also by the changing composition of the solution. We may write, therefore,

$$\frac{d \ln f}{d P} = \left(\frac{\partial \ln f}{\partial P}\right)_N + \left(\frac{\partial \ln f}{\partial \ln N}\right)_P \cdot \frac{d \ln N}{d P}. \tag{3}$$

The first term in the right hand member is given by

$$\left(\frac{\partial \ln f}{\partial P}\right)_N = \frac{\bar{v}}{RT}, \tag{4}$$

where $\bar{v}$ is the partial molal volume of this component in the solution (cf. p. 61). Substituting Equations 2, 3 and 4 in 1 gives

$$\frac{v'}{RT} = \frac{\bar{v}}{RT} + \left(\frac{\partial \ln f}{\partial \ln N}\right)_P \cdot \frac{d \ln N}{d P},$$

or transposed,

$$\frac{d \ln N}{d P} = \frac{v' - \bar{v}}{RT\left(\dfrac{\partial \ln f}{\partial \ln N}\right)_P}. \tag{5}$$

If Raoult's law holds

$$\left(\frac{\partial \ln f}{\partial \ln N}\right)_P = 1,$$

[42] Cf. Sorby, *Proc. Roy. Soc.*, **12**, 358 (1863); Braun, *Ann. Phys. Chem.* [3], **30**, 250 (1887).

and $\bar{v}$ usually equals v, the molal volume in the pure liquid state (cf. Chapter VI), so that we may simplify Equation 5 for such a case to

$$\frac{d \ln N}{d P} = \frac{v' - v}{RT}. \tag{6}$$

Since most substances expand on melting, v is usually larger than v' and hence v' — v is negative and the solubility *decreases* with pressure.

If there is a positive deviation from Raoult's law $\bar{v}$ is usually greater than v' so that v' — $\bar{v}$, in Equation 5 will be an even larger negative quantity than v' — v, in Equation 6. In such a case, also,

$$\frac{\partial \ln f}{\partial \ln N} < 1,$$

which will tend to increase the right hand member of Equation 5, and accentuate the diminution of solubility with increasing pressure.

If there is a negative deviation from Raoult's law $\bar{v}$ is usually less than v, and if it is also less than v' the right hand member of Equation 5 will be positive, giving an *increase* in solubility with pressure. In such a case

$$\frac{\partial \ln N}{\partial \ln P} > 1,$$

which tends to diminish the effect of pressure.

We may summarize by saying that *with systems which obey Raoult's law or which deviate from it in a positive direction, the usual effect of increasing the pressure upon the system will be to decrease the solubility, while with systems which deviate in the negative direction from Raoult's law increasing the pressure may cause an increase in solubility in some cases.* Of course, if the quantities in the right hand member of Equation 5 are known by experiment, the effect of pressure upon solubility can be calculated exactly.

If the pressure is applied to the solid phase only, as in the familiar experiment of drawing a wire through a block of ice without cutting the latter in two, then the effect is always to melt the solid, or increase its solubility, the increase being given by the equation

$$\frac{d \ln N}{d P} = \frac{v'}{RT \left(\dfrac{\partial \ln f}{\partial \ln N} \right)_P}. \tag{7}$$

SOLID SOLUTIONS.

(a) *Effect Upon Solubility.* Cases arise sometimes—frequently among the metals—when the solid phase in equilibrium with a solution is itself a solution, rather than one of the components in the pure solid state. The fugacity of X_2 from a solid solution, f_2', will, of course, be less than from its pure solid form, f^s, at the same temperature, so that the amount of X_2 in the liquid will also be less, or the temperature at which solid would separate from the solution will be higher than if the solid separating were pure.[43]

Since we know but little as yet concerning the departure of solid solutions from Raoult's law, it is hardly worth while to attempt to calculate the freezing-point-composition curves for such systems. The subject is worthy of systematic study.

(b) *Factors Governing the Formation of Solid Solutions.* The formation of solid solutions is favored by identity in crystal structure, and is most frequent with the metals, which crystallize, for the most part, in a few simple lattices. The chances of a triclinic crystal of one substance finding another capable of taking part in its structure are, of course, very remote.

Substances that are chemically very similar have greater chance of being crystallographically sufficiently similar to form solid solutions. The alums furnish familiar examples.

It seems probable, also, that solid solution is favored by similar atomic volumes and similar crystal forces, or cohesions, analogous to the internal pressures that play so important a rôle in liquids.

References: Jakob, *Z. Krist,* **56**, 295 (1921); Bain, *Trans. Am. Inst. Mining and Met. Eng.,* **1139 N**, Feb., 1922; Vegard, *Z. Physik.,* **5**, 17 (1921).

[43] Lewis and Randall, "Thermodynamics," p. 238, have given a formula for the freezing point lowering involving the distribution coefficient between the solid and liquid phases. Cf. also Smits, *Proc. Acad. Sci.,* Amsterdam, **23**, 679 (1921), *Verslag. Akad. Wetenschappen,* Amsterdam, **29**, 319 (1921).

Chapter XV.

Solubilities of Electrolytes.

The solubility of electrolytes involves so many factors that predictions are far more difficult than with the substances whose solubilities have been previously considered. Not only must we consider melting point, heat of fusion, internal pressure, polarity and solvation, but also a new factor, the ionization of the solute, which operates to increase the solubility. All chemists are familiar with the fact that an ionized electrolyte has an abnormally great lowering effect upon the activity of water, whether shown by the lowering of the vapor pressure, the lowering of the freezing point, the rise in boiling point, or any other method. For example, the lowering of vapor pressure of water produced by a binary electrolyte such as sodium chloride is approximately twice that produced by an un-ionized solute. Taking r_1 mols of water to 1 mol of solute, the mol fraction of the water is

$$N_1 = r_1/(r_1 + 1),$$ (1)

that of the solute is

$$N_2 = 1/(r_1 + 1).$$ (2)

But if the solute is completely dissociated into 2 ions, the total number of molecules is not $r_1 + 1$ but $r_1 + 2$, and if they are assumed to obey Raoult's law in the solution the activity of the water is

$$a_1 = r_1/(r_1 + 2).$$ (3)

For a salt dissociating into 3 ions, as does $BaCl_2$, the corresponding expression for the effect upon the activity of the solvent is

$$a_1 = r_1/(r_1 + 3).$$ (4)

Values of the apparent mol fraction, N_1, are plotted in Fig. 1 against a_1 for solutes giving 2 and 3 ions, respectively.

In order to calculate the solubility of the electrolyte from its melting point and heat of fusion we must have an expression for the activity of the *solute*. In harmony with our convention for non-electrolytes let us consider the fused electrolyte as the standard state and call its activity unity.[1] The activity of the electrolyte in its

---

[1] This must not be confused with the more usual assumption that the standard state is the infinitely dilute solution.

aqueous solution is then

$$a_2 = \left(\frac{2}{r_1 + 2}\right)^2, \tag{5}$$

for a binary electrolyte, or, in general,

$$a_2 = \left(\frac{v}{r_1 + v}\right)^v, \tag{6}$$

where v is the number of ions per molecule of salt.

We may accordingly calculate the ideal solubility of an ionized solid from its melting point and heat of fusion by using the activity as above expressed in place of N_2 in Equation IV-8, giving

$$\log\left(\frac{v}{r_1 + v}\right)^v = \frac{-L_f}{4.58}\left(\frac{1}{T} - \frac{1}{T_m}\right), \tag{7}$$

which can be solved for r_1; or replacing r_1 by $1/N_2 - 1$, Equation 2, we get

$$\log\left(\frac{v}{v - 1 + 1/N_2}\right)^v = \frac{-L_f}{4.58}\left(\frac{1}{T} - \frac{1}{T_m}\right), \tag{8}$$

which can be solved for N_2. This may be regarded as the ideal solubility equation for an electrolyte. Of course, there are many factors tending to produce deviation from this expression.

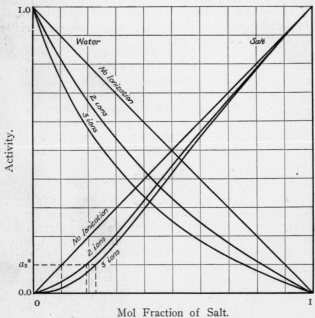

Fig. 1.—Effect of Ionization upon Solubility.

In Fig. 1 will be found curves for a_2 for $v = 2$ and $v = 3$. Suppose, now, that we are considering the solubility of a solid considerably below its melting point, whose activity is a_2^s in Fig. 1. It is evident that for any given value of the ordinate, a_2^s, the effect of ionization is to increase the value of the mol fraction of the solute, N_2. Another way of making this appear reasonable is to point out that, since the process of crystallization of the solute involves the simultaneous deposition of 2 or more ions, the dilution of these ions by the solvent diminishes the chance of this process occurring far more than in the case of the crystallization of an un-ionized substance, whose molecules are already formed in the solution.

The figure makes it evident, further, that the effect of ionization in increasing the solubility is greater the smaller the activity of the solid form, i.e., the higher the melting point of the solid.

SUMMARY OF FACTORS AFFECTING SOLUBILITIES OF SOLID ELECTROLYTES.

The effects just mentioned, together with the factors discussed in a general way in the earlier chapters may be summarized in the following more or less exact *rules concerning the solubility of a solid electrolyte expressed in terms of mol fraction.* (a) *The solubility is greater the lower the melting point and heat of fusion.* (*Where the solubility of a solid hydrate is being considered its own melting point rather than the melting point of the anhydrous solid should be used.*)

(b) *The effect of ionization is to increase solubility, especially with substances of low solubility.*

(c) *Hydration (or in general solvation) tends to increase solubility.*

(d) *Equal polarity of solvent and solute tends to increase solubility. Water is to be regarded as highly polar.*

(e) *Solvation, and hence solubility, is promoted by difference in the acidic and basic character of the solvent and solute; or by the existence in one of the components of an atom without the maximum possible number of surrounding electrons or atoms, as Al in $AlCl_3$, tending to form $AlCl_4^-$, or Cu^{++}, tending to form $Cu(NH_3)_4^{++}$, etc.*

ILLUSTRATIONS.

Table 1 illustrates the effect of some of the foregoing factors. We may note, first, that the substances of high melting point are all very insoluble. Although fused $BaSO_4$ is doubtless very polar, and a good conductor, it is but very slightly soluble because of the high melting point. The melting point of $CaSiO_3$ is a little lower, but the silicate radical being less strongly negative than the sulfate radical $CaSiO_3$ is less polar than $BaSO_4$ and hence less soluble. CaF_2 is highly polar and has a lower melting point, and is more soluble than $BaSO_4$, although still regarded as an "insoluble" substance; $CaCl_2$ on the other hand, has a much lower melting point and forms several hydrates so that the anhydrous salt is very soluble. In the case of the hexahydrate given at the top of the table, its own low melting point, 30°, is sufficient to account for its great solubility. $PbSO_4$ may be regarded as less polar than $BaSO_4$, so that its higher solubility may be attributed to its lower melting point. Ag_2S, though having a lower melting point than $PbSO_4$, is a compound of elements which are respectively not highly positive and negative, and hence the compound is not very polar, and not more than slightly soluble in water. Similar considerations may be invoked to account for the low solubilities of AgCl, $PbCl_2$ and HgI_2. Nitrates are always more polar than halides, hence $AgNO_3$ is more polar than AgCl, and aided by its low melting point, 218°, is very soluble in water. The solubility of AgF is to be attributed to the formation of the dihydrate. The effect of melting point upon the solubilities of similar anhydrous salts is striking, as shown by sodium chlorate, potassium chlorate and potassium iodate.

Considering the highly polar salts of known heat of fusion, ideal solubility calculated upon the assumption of complete ionization from Equation 7 is in several cases closer to the observed value than is the solubility figure which neglects ionization. However, the deviations are sufficient to indicate that the ions by no means obey Raoult's law in aqueous solutions of these concentrations. As a matter of fact,

TABLE 1.

SOLUBILITIES OF ELECTROLYTES IN WATER, AT 25°.

Solute	Melt. pt.	Heat of fusion [2]	Solubility, Mol Fraction.		
			No ioniz.	Ioniz.	Observ.
$CaCl_2.6H_2O$	30	8900	0.84	...	0.44
H_3BO_3	185	...	...	...	0.016
$AgNO_3$	218	2580	0.17	0.26	0.19
$NaClO_3$	255	5250	0.02	0.08	0.15
HgI_2	250	4440	0.04	0.11	2×10^{-6}
KNO_3	308	2570	0.12	0.21	0.063
$NaNO_3$	333	3690	0.03	0.10	0.162
$KClO_3$	360	...	...	...	0.013
$K_2Cr_2O_7$	397	2980	0.06	0.18	0.18
AgCl	455	3050	0.05	0.13	2×10^{-7}
$PbCl_2$	498	5150	5×10^{-3}	0.06	6.7×10^{-4}
KIO_3	560	...	...	...	0.008
KCl	772	6410	4×10^{-4}	0.01	0.088
$BaCO_3$	795	...	...	...	2×10^{-6}
Ag_2S	830	...	...	...	2×10^{-7}
$PbSO_4$	1100	...	...	...	3×10^{-6}
CaF_2	1400	...	...	...	4×10^{-6}
$CaSiO_3$	1510	...	...	...	$0+$
$BaSO_4$	1580	...	...	...	2×10^{-7}
Al_2O_3	2020	...	...	...	$0+$
Graphite	>3500	...	...	...	0

[2] Taken from the data given by Goodwin and Kalmus, *Phys. Rev.*, **28**, 1 (1909); see also Goodwin, *Trans. Am. Electrochem. Soc.*, **21**, 113 (1912), with the exception of the value for KCl by Plato, *Z. physik. Chem.*, **55**, 737 (1906), and that for $CaCl_2.6H_2O$, by Person, *Ann. chim. phys.* [3], **27**, 250 (1847).

various physical properties of aqueous solutions of different electrolytes are so far from uniform that it would be indeed strange if Raoult's law were obeyed by the ions in concentrated solutions. The different effects of salts upon the solubility of gases in water (Table XII-4) are of interest in this connection.

It must be frankly stated that the mere guess as to the polarity of a molten salt is not sufficient to explain all of the facts. For example, silver iodide, which we might expect to be weakly polar, is far *less* soluble in water than it would be if Raoult's law held, but it is at the same time far *more* soluble in liquid ammonia, which is also very polar, although less so than water. We may make a generalization that cannot be deduced from the simple criteria of polarity that we have announced, though it, too, ought ultimately to be brought into accord with the physical properties of the substances, namely, that the tendency to form hydrates, and hence to give negative deviations from Raoult's law and greater solubility in water solution, is greatest for elements at the top of the Periodic Table, whereas the tendency to unite with ammonia, and hence, presumably, to be more soluble in liquid ammonia, is greatest for elements at the bottom of the table. This is illustrated by the abnormally high solubility of magnesium chloride in water, on the one hand, and by the abnormally high solubility of mercuric iodide and silver iodide in liquid ammonia, on the other hand (cf. p. 120).

The effects of melting point and hydration are illustrated by the salts of the alkali metals, in Table 2, where the highly polar character of all of the compounds minimizes the effect of differences in polarity such as must be considered more carefully with salts of weak acids or bases. Starting with the fluorides, we see a rapidly increasing solubility as we go from the rather insoluble LiF to the very soluble CsF, which is in accord both with the considerable decrease in melting point and with the hydration which appears with $KF.2H_2O$ and doubtless continues with the next two members. With the chlorides the hydration is found to be greatest with the first member, LiCl, for some reason which we would be pleased to explain, appearing only below $0.15°$ with NaCl, and not at all with the others. This, considered alone, would indicate a decreasing solubility as we proceed from LiCl to CsCl, but the melting points, falling off from NaCl to CsCl, favor an increasing solubility. The combined effect of these to opposing factors is to give a minimum with KCl. The bromides behave similarly, but here the hydration is stronger, $NaBr.2H_2O$ being stable up to $50.7°$, so that the minimum is shifted to RbCl. With the iodides the hydration is still greater and overbalances the effect of melting point throughout. With the nitrates the decreasing hydration and increasing melting points combine to give a somewhat irregularly decreasing solubility. The sulfates show a less regular behavior with respect to both melting point and hydration, and it is therefore not surprising to find the solubilities likewise less regular.

TABLE 2.

SOLUBILITIES OF SALTS OF ALKALI METALS. MOL FRACTION AT 25°.

Figures in parenthesis denote number of molecules of water in solid phase.

		Li	Na	K	Rb	Cs
Fluorides	m. pt....	~1000	980	860	750	...
	solubility..	0.010	0.018	0.237(2)	(Very sol.)	(Very sol.)
Chlorides	m. pt......	613	801	773	714	645
	solubility..	0.261(2)	0.101	0.088	0.123	0.153
Bromides	m. pt......	442	760	730	685	...
	solubility..	0.275(2)	0.141(2)	0.093	0.056	0.104
Iodides	m. pt......	446[3]	752	698	642	621
	solubility..	0.182(3)	0.181(2)	0.138	0.122	0.053
Nitrates	m. pt......	261[4]	316	335	....	414
	solubility..	0.152(3)	0.162	0.063	0.073	0.025
Sulfates	m. pt......	859	880	1050	1074	1019
	solubility..	0.052(1)	0.061[5]	0.012	0.033	0.083

EFFECT OF RELATIVE POSITIVE AND NEGATIVE CHARACTERS OF SOLVENT
AND SOLUTE.

The effect of diversity in positive and negative character in pro-
moting compound formation, and hence solubility, which has already
been discussed (Chapter X), has been studied in some detail by Kendall
and coworkers,[6] who point out particularly that electrode potentials
are of value in determining this diversity.   Thus, *if a salt, RX, is dissolved in a solvent HX, compound formation, and hence solubility, are*

TABLE 3.

SOLUBILITIES OF SULFATES IN SULFURIC ACID.[7]

Metal	Electrode potential	Solubility Mol percent, 25°	Mols H_2SO_4 in solid phase
Li	— 2.96	14.28	2
K	— 2.92	9.24	3
Ba	— 2.8 (?)	8.85	3
Na	— 2.71	5.28	9/2
Ca	— 2.5 (?)	5.16	3
Mg	— 1.55	0.18	3
Al	— 1.34	<0.01	0
Zn	— 0.76	0.17	X
Fe (Fe^{++})...............	— 0.44	0.17	X
Ni	— 0.22	Very small	0
Pb	— 0.13	Small	0
Fe (Fe^{+++})...............	— 0.44	<0.01	0
Cu	+ 0.35	0.08	0
Hg (Hg$_2^{++}$)	+ 0.80	0.78	1
Ag	+ 0.80	9.11	2
Hg (Hg^{++})	+ 0.86	0.02	0

[3] Melting point of trihydrate 73°.
[4] Melting point of trihydrate 30°.
[5] Supersaturated with respect to dekahydrate.
[6] Loc. cit., p. 86, especially Kendall, Davidson and Adler, *J. Am. Chem. Soc.*,
43, 1481 (1921).
[7] Kendall and Davidson, *J. Am. Chem. Soc.*, **43**, 979 (1921).

TABLE 4.

SOLUBILITIES OF FORMATES IN FORMIC ACID.[8]

Metal	Electrode potential	Solubility Mol percent, 25°	Mols HCOOH in solid phase
Li	— 2.96	23.7	0
K	— 2.92	25.5	1
Ba	— 2.8 (?)	9.8	1
Na	— 2.71	21.3	2
Ca	— 2.5 (?)	1.7	0
Mg	— 1.55	0.2	0
Zn	— 0.76	<0.1	0
Ni	— 0.22	<0.1	0
Pb	— 0.13	0.2	0
Cu	+ 0.35	<0.1	0

promoted by diversity between the electrode potentials of R and H.
This is illustrated by the data given in Tables 3 and 4.

Kendall, Davidson and Adler apply similar considerations to more complex systems such as fluorides in water. Table 5 gives the series they cite as one illustration.

We have added the melting points of the anhydrous solids to show that the irregularities in the solubilities of the series are to be expected on the basis of the differences in melting points. The higher melting point of BaF_2, for example, would tend to make it less soluble than NaF, in spite of the greater hydration of the former which the theory of these authors demands.

CHANGE OF SOLUBILITY WITH TEMPERATURE.

The general relations outlined in Chapter V for the effect of temperature upon the solubility of solids may be applied to the specific field here under discussion. The solubility of the different forms of sodium sulfate may be selected to illustrate two extreme types. The very rapid increase in solubility of the dekahydrate with increasing temperature is not strange, as we should expect it, like most highly hydrated salts, to have a low melting point. The fact that transition

TABLE 5.

SOLUBILITIES OF FLUORIDES IN WATER.

Salt	Solubility Mol percent, 18°	Solid phase	Melting point
KF	14.79	$KF.4H_2O$	860 (anhydrous)
BaF_2	0.0166	BaF_2	1280
NaF	1.85	NaF	980
SrF_2	0.0017	SrF_2	1200
CaF_2	0.00037	CaF_2	1400
AgF	18.0 (approx.)	$AgF.4H_2O$	435 (anhydrous)

[8] Kendall and Adler, *J. Am. Chem. Soc.*, **43**, 1470 (1921). A similar table is there given for hydroxides in water.

of the hydrate to the anhydrous salt occurs a little before congruent melting is attained is immaterial to the point of view.

The anhydrous salt, the stable phase above 32°, shows a negative temperature coefficient, which is a more unusual phenomenon. Its rather high melting point, 884°, considered by itself, would lead us to expect its solubility to be rather small and to increase with the temperature. On the other hand, the tendency to hydration, shown by the existence of the solid dekahydrate, undoubtedly persists in solution above the transition temperature of the hydrated to the anhydrous solid. This hydration operates to increase the solubility of the anhydrous salt far above the value it would otherwise have, though to a less and less extent as the temperature increases, so that the solubility *decreases* with the temperature, the decrease in hydration more than counter-balancing the increase that would occur in the absence of any considerable hydration.

Potassium sulfate gives no solid hydrate, and not only does its solubility increase with temperature but it is much smaller than that of sodium sulfate, although this latter fact is partly due to its higher melting point, 1074°.

Other salts showing negative temperature coefficients of solubility are $CdSO_4$, $MgSO_4$, $CaSO_4$, $ZnSO_4.H_2O$, $CdSO_4.H_2O$, all of which at lower temperatures form solid hydrates with more water. Still other salts, though not showing negative solubility coefficients, show abnormally small positive coefficients for the same reason. These include NaCl, NaOH, $ZnCl_2$, $CdCl_2.H_2O$, NaBr, NaI, $CaCl_2.H_2O$ and LiCl. All of these likewise form higher hydrates at lower temperatures. The difference between the temperature coefficients of NaCl and KCl is very familiar, and is undoubtedly due to the increasing hydration of NaCl as the temperature is lowered, counteracting almost completely the normal decrease shown by KCl and which would otherwise be shown by NaCl, and yielding finally, at 0.15° and below, the hydrate $NaCl.2H_2O$.

SOLUBILITIES IN THE ALCOHOLS.

In changing the solvent from water to the aliphatic alcohols the principal effect upon solubilities may be attributed to the decrease in polar character in the order water, methyl alcohol, ethyl alcohol, etc., causing a corresponding decrease in the solubility, as illustrated in Table 6, except with LiI, where the opposite order is seen, due probably to solvation.

The change in solubility in going from the chloride of one alkali metal to that of the next varies in the same way with the alcohols as with water, due to the combined effect of the melting point and solvation, as already explained, p. 168, giving a minimum with KCl as illustrated in Table 7.

All of these solvents evidently form solvates with LiCl in solution, for solid phases with solvent of crystallization exist at lower tem-

TABLE 6.
SOLUBILITIES,[9] MOL FRACTIONS AT 25°.
Figures in parenthesis denote mols of solvent identified in solid phase.

Solute	H_2O	CH_3OH	C_2H_5OH	C_3H_7OH	$C_5H_{11}OH$
LiCl	0.261(1)	0.238 [10]	0.219 [10]	0.191	0.159
NaCl	0.101	0.0072	0.00051	0.00012	0.00007
KCl	0.088	0.0023	0.00013	0.000032	0.000001
LiI	0.182(3)	0.452	0.477	0.319(4)	0.528
NaI	0.181(3)	0.162	0.124(2)	0.100	0.088
KI	0.138	0.0344	0.0059	0.0015	0.00052

TABLE 7.
SOLUBILITIES, MOL FRACTIONS AT 25°.
Figures in parenthesis denote mols solvent in solid phase.

Solvents	LiCl	NaCl	KCl	RbCl	CsCl
H_2O [11]	0.261(1)	0.101	0.088	0.123	0.153
CH_3OH [12]	0.238 [14]	0.0072	0.0023	0.0036	0.0065 [13]
C_2H_5OH [12]	0.219 [14]	0.00051	0.00013	0.0003	....
C_3H_7OH [12]	0.191	0.00012	0.000032	0.00007	....
$C_5H_{11}OH$ [12]	0.159	0.00007	0.000001	0.00002	....

peratures if not at 25°, thus with C_2H_5OH below 17° the solid phase is $LiCl.4C_2H_5OH$.

SOLVENTS OF LOW POLARITY.

These usually exert but slight solvent action upon the highly polar electrolytes. Where an exception is found it can doubtless invariably be traced to solvation. An interesting case of this sort is presented by $AgClO_4$, which is not only very soluble in water but also in benzene,[15] due to the formation in both cases of compounds with the solvent, $AgClO_4.H_2O$ and $AgClO_4.C_6H_6$. The latter compound is very unusual, as benzene is not sufficiently polar to form many such combinations. The discovery of the reasons for their occurrence would make possible great progress in the prediction of solubilities.

There are many salts of such low polarity as to be very appreciably soluble in solvents such as benzene in so far as their melting points are not too high. This is illustrated in Table 8 for solubilities of CdI_2 and the mercuric halides, arranged in order of decreasing polarity from left to right. We see that while the solubilities in water,

[9] Data for the alcohols from Turner and Bissett, *J. Chem. Soc.,* **103,** 1904 (1913). The author is indebted to Mr. Waldo M. Westwater for the calculations.
[10] A solvate exists at a lower temperature.
[11] Cf. Table 2.
[12] Cf. Table 6.
[13] Determined by Waldo M. Westwater.
[14] A solvated solid phase exists at a lower temperature.
[15] Hill, *J. Am. Chem. Soc.,* **44,** 1163 (1922).

TABLE 8.[16]

SOLUBILITIES, MOL FRACTIONS AT 25°.

Solvent	Melt. pt.	CdI_2 404	$HgCl_2$ 277	$HgBr_2$ 235	HgI_2 250
Water		0.042	0.0053	0.00169	2.4×10^{-6}
Acetone		0.048	0.25	0.079	0.0044
Alcohol		0.121	0.078	0.032	0.0022
Ethylene bromide		....	0.011	0.012	0.0031
Ether		....	0.0186	0.00016	0.00014
Benzene		0.0001	0.00174	0.00171	0.00379
Carbon tetrachloride		....	0.000011	0.000013	0.00002
Ideal		....	....	....	0.04

acetone and alcohol decrease, in spite of the decrease in melting point, the solubilities in benzene and carbon tetrachloride increase.

These halides in the molten state would undoubtedly give evidence of higher internal pressure than such a solvent as benzene, hence it is not surprising to find that ethylene bromide is a much better solvent than benzene. Carbon tetrachloride is a poor solvent for these halides because of a very low polarity as well as internal pressure.

Salts like ferric chloride and zinc chloride have sufficiently low melting points and sufficiently low polarities to be soluble in alcohols, in acetone, pyridin, ethyl acetate and ether, and the former is even slightly soluble in benzene.

SOLUBILITIES IN LIQUID AMMONIA.

There are almost no quantitative data upon the solubilities in liquid ammonia, and very little upon the existence of solid ammoniates (analogous to hydrates). Such information as we have, however, seems to be in accord with the following characteristics of ammonia:

(a) It is somewhat less polar than water.

(b) It has a lower internal pressure.

(c) It is a more basic solvent.

Referring to the precipitation experiments of Franklin and Kraus,[17] we find that the sulfates, carbonates, phosphates, oxalates and alkali hydroxides are insoluble. These are substances which have high surface tensions in the molten state, and which therefore require a solvent of high internal pressure and polarity to dissociate and dissolve them.

The alkali hydroxides and amids are naturally less solvated and dissolved by such a basic solvent, while the acids, which solvate to form ammonium salts, are easily soluble. We may reasonably expect that in an acidic solvent, like HCN or SO_2, the reverse would be true, i.e., the bases would be more and the acids less soluble.

Such salts as PbI_2, AgCl, AgI and the cupric halides are easily

[16] The author is indebted to Mr. R. M. Buffington for the preparation of this table.

[17] Franklin and Kraus, *Am. Chem. J.*, **21**, 1, 8 (1899).

soluble in ammonia. They are all rather easily melted, and are less polar than most salts, and most of them are undoubtedly solvated, as shown by their ability to absorb ammonia gas, and by their greater solubility in aqua ammonia than in water.

A very striking feature is the relatively great solubility of iodides in ammonia, as well as in the less polar solvents. Unlike water, liquid ammonia dissolves more AgI than AgCl. This may be connected, first, with the smaller polarity of iodides than bromides or chlorides, and second, with the evidently smaller attractive forces in iodides, as shown by various criteria,[18] but especially by the small surface tensions of aqueous solutions of iodides, and their tendency to increase the solubility in water of gases and non-polar liquids. The same is true of thiocyanates, and to a lesser degree of nitrates, and these salts are likewise soluble in liquid ammonia.

SOLUBILITIES OF FUSED SALTS IN EACH OTHER.

These have until recently received but little attention, and but few cases of incomplete immiscibility were known. Through the work of Kendall, Crittenden and Miller,[19] 17 such cases have been discovered, all of which contain either $AlCl_3$ or $AlBr_3$ as one of the components. These salts are to be regarded as not very polar (cf. Chapter X), and hence hardly to be expected to mix with other more polar fused salts, or even with other compounds of low polarity, but greatly different internal pressure. We would, of course, expect $SnCl_4$ to behave in a similar manner. The authors referred to above have made a rough estimate of the relative internal pressures by means of the expression $(5200 + 30t_b)/v$, obtaining the following figures:

TABLE 9.
RELATIVE INTERNAL PRESSURES OF FUSED SALTS.

$SnCl_4$	1,550	$BiBr_3$	4,900	AgBr	25,000
$SnBr_4$	1,770	$HgCl_2$	5,900	KCl	26,300
$AsBr_3$	2,800	$SnBr_2$	9,000	CuCl	27,100
$AlBr_3$	3,050	$ZnBr_2$	9,500	AgCl	28,200
$SbBr_3$	3,250	HgBr	10,000	NaBr	28,400
$SbCl_3$	3,320	HgCl	10,400	LiBr	35,600
$AlCl_3$	4,120	$CdBr_2$	10,700	NaCl	37,100
$HgBr_2$	4,400	TlCl	16,200	LiCl	44,800
		KBr	21,700		

One of the 2 liquid phases obtained was chiefly the aluminum halide, the other, usually a compound, such as $TlBr.AlBr_3$, $HgBr.AlBr_3$, $BaBr_2.2AlBr_3$, $AgBr.4AlBr_3$, $XKCl.yAlCl_3$, etc., which was soluble in excess of the more polar component. It would be expected that such a compound would be far more polar than the less polar component, so that it is not surprising that these compounds are not completely soluble in the less polar aluminum halide.

[18] Cf. T. W. Richards, *J. Am. Chem. Soc.*, **45**, 422 (1923).
[19] Kendall, Crittenden and Miller, *J. Am. Chem. Soc.*, **45**, 963 (1923).

Effect of a Third Component Upon the Solubility of an Electrolyte in Water.

The previous chapters have made it evident that the addition of a less polar substance to water will usually lower the solubilities of electrolytes. For example, NaCl can be partly precipitated from its saturated aqueous solution by the addition of alcohol [20] or ether. This is simply the reverse of the familiar "salting out" of, say, ether from water by the addition of salt.

The greatest uncertainty enters when the added third substance is itself an electrolyte. Here we are accustomed to make joint use of the ionic theory and the mass law in the form which assumes that activity is proportional to concentration. Accordingly, we predict that electrolytes with common ions diminish each other's solubility, and that electrolytes with no common ions increase each other's solubility.[21] This is usually the case. Thus, the addition of a small quantity of either NaCl or $AgNO_3$ decreases the solubility of AgCl. HCl gas precipitates NaCl from its saturated aqueous solution. On the other hand the solubility of AgCl is increased by the presence of KNO_3. That of TlCl is increased by KNO_3, $NaC_2H_3O_2$ and $CdSO_4$, to the greatest extent in the last case, since $CdCl_2$ is a rather weak salt and its formation removes Cl^- from the solution allowing more TlCl to dissolve than in the other cases.

Lewis and Randall [22] have made a very extensive study of activities of electrolytes which has led to a rather simple method for calculating the effect of one electrolyte upon the solubility of another. It will be impossible, in the space here devoted, to give a complete exposition of their methods, so that we will give only a brief outline, advising reference to the original, which is readily available, for fuller details.

In the study of electrolytes it is convenient, or at least customary, to define the ideal solution in a slightly different way from that used earlier in this book. Instead of using Raoult's law for the ions, writing the activity of each ion equal to its mol fraction, Equation III-19, we write the activity of each ion as equal to its stoichiometrical molality, i.e., the number of formula mols per 1000 g. of water. In dilute solutions these definitions differ only by the factor 55.51, the number of mols of water in 1000 g., since $N_2 = \dfrac{n_2}{n_1 + n_2}$, and $m = \dfrac{n_2}{55.51 + n_2}$, and n_2 is small compared with 55.51

A positive ion gives an ideal solution by definition when its activity equals its stoichiometric molality, or $a_+ = m_+$. For a negative ion we write similarly $a_- = m_-$. The activities of the molecule and its ions

---

[20] E.g., Bodländer, *Z. physik. Chem.*, **7**, 308 (1891).

[21] Nernst, *Z. physik. Chem.*, **4**, 379 (1889) ; A. A. Noyes, *Z. physik. Chem.*, **6**, 262 (1890).

[22] G. N. Lewis and Merle Randall, *J. Am. Chem. Soc.*, **43**, 1112 (1921). "Thermodynamics," McGraw-Hill Co., 1923, Chap. XXVIII.

for a binary electrolyte like KCl are related by the mass law expression

$$\frac{a_+a_-}{a_2} = K. \tag{9}$$

Since we know nothing definite about the actual concentration of undissociated molecules it is convenient to define their activity by putting $K = 1$ and writing $a_+a_- = a_2$. $\tag{10}$
When the solution becomes infinitely dilute it becomes ideal and $a_+ = a_- = m = a_2^{1/2}$. In ordinary dilute solutions the ions may not have equal activities but it suffices for our purpose to use the geometrical mean of the ionic activities, $a_\pm = \sqrt{a_+a_-} = a_2^{1/2}$. $\tag{11}$

The degree of dissociation, so much used in the literature, is replaced by the *thermodynamic degree of dissociation,* or activity coefficient, γ, which becomes unity at infinite dilution, when the solution becomes ideal. For a binary electrolyte, where the molality of each ion is the stoichiometric molality of the electrolyte, we have $\gamma = a_\pm/m$. When the electrolyte is more complicated m must be replaced by the mean molality, $m_\pm$. For a uni-bivalent salt, such as $BaCl_2$, since the molality of Ba is m, that of Cl^- is $2m$, we have $m_\pm = (m \times \overline{2m^2})^{1/3}$. For $La_2(SO_4)_3$ we would have

$$m_\pm = (\overline{2m^2} \times \overline{3m^3})^{1/5}.$$

If some other sulfate were likewise present the molality of sulfate ion would have to be obtained by adding the molalities of the ions from each salt. Thus, in 0.01 molal $La_2(SO_4)_3$ containing likewise 0.02 molal K_2SO_4, the total molality of sulfate ion would be $3 \times 0.01 + 0.02$ or 0.05. Moreover, since m_+ for La^{+++} in this solution is 0.02, the mean molality of the ions of $La_2(SO_4)_3$ would be

$$(\overline{0.02^2} \times \overline{0.05^3})^{1/5} \text{ or } 0.0232.$$

In general, if the numbers of ions yielded by one mol of electrolyte are ν_+ and ν_- respectively, we may write

$$m_\pm = (m_+^{\nu_+} m_-^{\nu_-})^{1/\nu} \tag{12}$$

where ν is the total number of ions, $\nu_+ + \nu_-$. The activity coefficient is in general, $\gamma = a_\pm/m_\pm$. $\tag{13}$

A new function, the *ionic strength,* μ, is next introduced. It is defined as one half of the sum of the stoichiometrical molalities of all of the ions present in a solution, each multiplied by the square of its valence or charge. It may be defined formally by the expression

$$\mu = \tfrac{1}{2}\,(m_+\nu_+^2 + m_+'\nu_+'^2 + \ldots m_-\nu_-^2 + m_-'\nu_-'^2 + \ldots). \tag{14}$$

The following examples will serve as illustration. In 0.02 molal KCl $m_+ = m_- = 0.02$. so that $\mu = \tfrac{1}{2}(0.02 \times 1^2 + 0.02 \times 1^2) = 0.02$. In 0.02 molal $BaCl_2$. $m_+ = 0.02$ and $\nu_+ = 2$; $m_- = 0.04$ and $\nu_- = 1$, hence $\mu = \frac{1}{2}(0.02 \times 2^2 + 0.04) = 0.06$. In a solution containing both 0.02 molal K_2SO_4 and 0.05 molal NaCl, $m_+ = 0.04$ for K^+ and 0.05 for Na^+; $m_- = 0.02$ for SO_4^{--} and 0.05 for Cl^-, hence $\mu = \frac{1}{2}(0.04 + 0.05 + 0.02 \times 4 + 0.05) = 0.11$. For a solution containing both 0.02 molal K_2SO_4 and 0.01 molal $MgSO_4$, the molalities of K^+, Mg^{++} and SO_4^{--} are respectively 0.04, 0.01 and 0.03, hence $\mu = \frac{1}{2}(0.04 + 0.01 \times 4 + 0.03 \times 4) = 0.10$.

The empirical rule discovered by Lewis and Randall may now be expressed as follows: *in dilute solutions the activity coefficient of a given strong electrolyte is the same in all solutions of equal ionic strength.* Moreover, since the activity of a salt in a solution in equi-

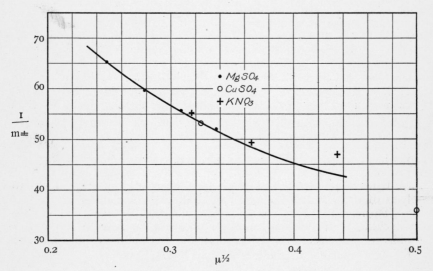

FIG. 2.—Solubilities of CaSO₄ in Other Electrolytes.

librium with its pure solid form is constant at any one temperature, we see by Equation 13 that the activity coefficient is proportional to the mean molality, hence it follows from the above rule that if values of $1/m_\pm$ for the solubility of a given rather insoluble electrolyte in solutions of others are plotted against μ (or better $\mu^{\frac{1}{2}}$ to get the more linear relation) the points should all fall on the same curve regardless of the nature of the added electrolytes.

Table 10 contains the results of measurements by Harkins and Paine [23] on the solubility of $CaSO_4$ in the presence of $MgSO_4$, $CuSO_4$ and KNO_3, together with values of $1/m_\pm$ and μ calculated from them. In Fig. 2 are plotted these values of $1/m_\pm$ against $\mu^{\frac{1}{2}}$. It will be seen that for the more dilute solutions the points fall very closely upon the same curve. Other examples are given by Lewis and Randall

[23] Harkins and Paine, *J. Am. Chem. Soc.*, **41**, 1155 (1919).

TABLE 10.

Solubility of CaSO₄ in Presence of Other Salts at 25°.

Added	Salt molality	Molality of Ca++	$\dfrac{1}{m_\pm}$	μ
None	....	0.01535	65.15	0.0614
MgSO₄	0.00502	0.01441	59.77	0.0777
	0.01012	0.01362	55.59	0.0950
	0.01528	0.01310	51.92	0.1135
CuSO₄	0.01254	0.01360	53.08	0.1046
	0.05014	0.01239	35.97	0.250
	0.1010	0.01242	26.67	0.454
	0.2120	0.01329	12.92	0.901
	0.9771	0.01654	7.81	3.974
KNO₃	0 02766	0.01812	55.19	0.1001
	0.05293	0.02019	49.53	0.1337
	0.1038	0.02130	46.95	0.1890

showing similar good agreement with their rule. It is obvious that having established the curve with $MgSO_4$ we could have used it to calculate the effect of $CuSO_4$ or KNO_3 upon the solubility of $CaSO_4$. We may therefore feel considerable confidence that we could reverse the above calculation and predict the effect of some other added electrolyte upon the solubility of $CaSO_4$. (In making such a calculation it will prove most convenient to use the method of successive approximations.)

It may be added that the ionic strength rule holds best for electrolytes of the same general type and strength.

Turning to more concentrated solutions, we encounter greater difficulties in predicting the effect of one electrolyte upon the solubility of another. A large part of the education of the chemist is devoted to gaining experience in this direction. He learns that a precipitate is made more soluble by the addition of any substance with which it tends to form (a) a weak salt, (b) a weak acid, (c) a weak base, (d) a complex ion or (e) a volatile substance,[24] and he must learn what ions are capable of uniting to form substances belonging to any of the above classes. It would carry us too far, however, to enter upon a general discussion of this phase of the problem of solubility, and we will simply call attention to a few additional consequences of the principles mentioned in Chapter X.

The solubility of AgCl is first diminished by the addition of a chloride, but as more chloride is added its solubility is greatly increased. Kendall, Davidson and Adler[25] have called attention to the relation between the relative effectiveness of HCl, $CaCl_2$, $NaCl$, $SrCl_2$, $BaCl_2$, KCl and NH_4Cl in increasing the solubility of AgCl in the order given, HCl having the least effect,[26] and the electrode potential series of the positive constituents, which is Ag, H, Ca, Na or Sr, Ba,

---

[24] Cf. Hildebrand, "Principles of Chemistry," Macmillan, 1918, Chap. XIII.
[25] Kendall, Davidson and Adler, *J. Am. Chem. Soc.*, **43**, 1481 (1921).
[26] Forbes, *ibid.*, **33**, 1937 (1911).

K, (NH$_4$?).   Therefore HCl and AgCl are close together in an electro-chemical sense, NaCl and AgCl much farther apart and KCl and AgCl still more so.   This increasing diversity is well correlated with the increasing tendency towards complex formation and increased solubility.   Many instances of similar behavior are known.

Space does not permit of the discussion of other investigations upon the effect of one electrolyte upon the solubility of another.   The reader who is interested in this particular topic should, however, make himself familiar with the studies of Brönsted.[27]

[27] Brönsted, *J. Am. Chem. Soc.*, **42**, 761, 1468 (1920) ; **43**, 2265 (1921) ; **44**, 877, 938 (1922).   See also A. A. Noyes and W. C. Bray, *J. Am. Chem. Soc.*, **33**, 1643 (1911) ; Noyes, Boggs, Farrell and Stewart, *ibid.*, **33**, 1650 (1911) ; Bray and Winninghoff, *ibid.*, **33**, 1663 (1911) ; Bray, *ibid.*, **33**, 1673 (1911) ; Harkins, *ibid.*, **33**, 1807 (1911) ; Harkins and Winninghoff, *ibid.*, **33**, 1827 (1911) ; Harkins, *ibid.*, **33**, 1836 (1911) ; Harkins and Pierce, *ibid.*, **37**, 2679 (1916) ; Harkins and Paine, *ibid.*, **41**, 1155 (1919).

Chapter XVI.

Metallic Solutions.

Metallic solutions offer a particularly inviting field for the application of a theory of solubility, because a large amount of data is available, and also because the metals differ among themselves in surface tension, compressibility, expansion, internal pressure and other characteristics far more than do the familiar non-metallic liquids, so that they offer a much more severe test of a theory than do most non-metallic solutions. For example, although but few non-metallic liquids, excluding water, are sufficiently unalike to yield two liquid phases, there are known no less than 47 metallic pairs which are incompletely miscible in the liquid state.

We do not have data upon the coefficients of compressibility and expansion for molten metals necessary for the calculation of their internal pressures by the expression $T\alpha/\beta$ (pp. 70, 103) except for mercury, where the value is 13,200 megabars. This is several times as large as the values for the common non-metallic liquids, which explains, at least partly, their immiscibility with mercury. We may perhaps get a rough idea of the internal pressures of liquid metals from the values of α/β of their solid forms. Table I gives some figures of this sort taken from a paper by T. W. Richards.[1] We may also note that the tensile strengths of the metals are in somewhat the same order, Ni, Pt, Fe and Cu, for example, having high, Pb, Na, Bi, etc., low tensile strengths.

The surface tension of molten metals may be expected to give a truer indication of the internal forces in the case of molten metals than it does in the case of most other liquids, because the molecules are simple and symmetrical and little or no orientation should take place in the surface. We may use the expression $\gamma/v^{\frac{1}{3}}$, or, where data are available, $E_\sigma/v^{\frac{1}{3}}$ (cf. Chapter IX). We have accurate measurements by Hogness[2] for Hg, Bi, Cd, Pb, Sn and Zn. Most values for the other metals are unsatisfactory and conflicting due, partly at least, to failure to prevent the formation of an oxide film. Table 2 gives values for a number of the more important metals. On account of the difference in temperature the magnitude of $\gamma/v^{\frac{1}{3}}$ for the first five metals is much less than it would be if all of the metals in the table could be compared at the same temperature; accordingly we are

[1] T. W. Richards, *J. Am. Chem. Soc.*, **37**, 1643 (1915).
[2] Hogness, *J. Am. Chem. Soc.*, **43**, 1621 (1921).

TABLE 1.

RELATIVE INTERNAL PRESSURES OF SOLID METALS ESTIMATED FROM EXPANSION AND COMPRESSIBILITY.

	$\alpha.10^6$	$\beta.10^8$	α/β
Nickel	42	43	98
Silicon	23	32	72
Platinum	27	38	71
Gold	43	64	67
Copper	50	75	67
Iron	36	60	60
Silver	57	101	56
Zinc	87	170	51
Aluminum	72	147	49
Mercury (liq.)	180	395	46
Lead	88	233	38
Cadmium	74	210	35
Tin	67	190	35
Sodium	220	1560	14
Bismuth	40	300	12.5
Potassium	250	3170	7.9
Cesium	330?	6100	5.4

justified in concluding that their internal pressures would be found higher, at the same temperature, than those of the second group, Zn-Bi inclusive. It will be noted that the order is not very different from that given in Table 1, where, of course, crystal structure introduces disturbing factors.

The only other method applicable to the metals is the one using heat of vaporization (cf. Chapter IX). Table 3 gives values of L/v, which again show approximately the same order except that the most volatile, Hg and Cd, are shifted considerably downwards. Table 2, however, seems to be more closely correlated with our present knowledge of intermetallic systems.

TABLE 2.

RELATIVE INTERNAL PRESSURES OF METALS FROM SURFACE TENSIONS.

	γ	t	E_σ	$\gamma/v^{1/3}$	$E_\sigma/v^{1/3}$
Platinum	1819 [3]	1800	...	...	...
Iron	950 [3]	1600	...	490	...
Silver	782 [3]	1000	...	348	...
Copper	581 [3]	1100	...	294	...
Gold	612 [4]	1070	...	282	...
Zinc	755	450	820	350	380
Cadmium	622	450	662	256	274
Mercury	393	350	580	157	232
Tin	514	450	572	198	222
Lead	438	450	494	163	182
Bismuth	367	450	413	133	150
Potassium	412 [3]	62	...	114	...
Sodium	294 [3]	90	...	92	...

[3] Quincke, *Pogg. Ann.*, **135**, 642 (1868); **138**, 141 (1869).
[4] Heydweiler, *Wied. Ann.*, **62**, 694 (1897).

TABLE 3.

RELATIVE INTERNAL PRESSURES OF METALS FROM HEAT OF VAPORIZATION.

	L^5	v	t	L/v
Nickel	69,200	6.71	1,450	10,300
Copper	66,900	7.56	1,083	8,850
Iron	70,600	8.11	1,530	8,700
Silver	61,800	11.3	961	5,500
Aluminum	52,500	11.2	658	4,560
Tin	66,200	16.9	232	3,920
Zinc	28,800	10.1	419	2,850
Lead	45,700	20.0	327	2,410
Thallium	39,600	17.2	302	2,300
Bismuth	42,200	20.8	269	2,030
Cadmium	25,000	14.1	321	1,770
Mercury	14,400	15.5	300	973

We will now proceed to examine the solubility data to determine how far the arrangement in these tables corresponds to the mutual solubilities of the metals. We must be prepared, of course, to find solubilities greater than internal pressure differences alone would lead us to expect, due to compound formation, even though the attractions between the components may be insufficient to cause the separation in the solid state of any recognizable compounds. If the electron theory were more highly developed with reference to liquid metals we would doubtless be better prepared than we now are to predict compound formation and its attendant effects upon solubility. There is great need for enlightenment regarding the nature of intermetallic compounds.[6]

We will first consider the group of metals, Zn, Cd, Hg, Sn, Pb, Bi, which, according to Table 2, have internal pressures decreasing in that order. We have very accurate data by Taylor, soon to be published, concerning the activities, a, of these metals in a number of their liquid alloys, obtained by measuring e.m.f's of concentration cells. Taylor found that the pairs given below in Table 4 give positive deviations from Raoult's law of the normal type. Writing Raoult's law as $a = N$, where N is mol fraction, the deviation may be expressed by the value of $\log (a/N)$.

TABLE 4.

ACTIVITY COEFFICIENTS IN VARIOUS ALLOYS.

Alloy	t	$\log a/N$ for Cd $N_{Cd} = 0.1$	$N_{Cd} = 0.2$	$\Delta(E_\sigma/v^{1/3})$
Cd–Sn	483	0.228	0.185	52
Cd–Pb	480	0.455	0.369	92
Cd–Zn	466	0.560	0.373	106

		$\log a/N$ for Sn $N_{Sn} = 0.1$	$N_{Sn} = 0.2$	
Sn–Zn	466	0.460	0.274	158
Sn–Cd	463	0.251	0.185	52

[5] Hildebrand, *J. Am. Chem. Soc.*, **40**, 45 (1918).
[6] Cf. However Kraus, *J. Am. Chem. Soc.*, **44**, 1216 (1922).

The values of a/N for the three Cd alloys are in the same order as, although not strictly proportional to, the differences between the internal pressures of the components, using $E_\sigma/v^{\frac{1}{3}}$ to indicate the latter. The same is true for the two Sn-alloys. Taylor also obtained results for Cd-Bi alloys. We might expect here to find a large deviation on account of their large internal pressure difference. As a matter of fact the deviation from Raoult's law is small, but of so irregular a type as to make its non-conformity to the internal pressure theory not at all strange. The phenomena in this mixture are evidently rather complex.

Freezing point-composition diagrams are available which permit us to give the freezing point lowering for a given solvent and a series of solutes at a fixed composition, which, in the absence of "chemical" effects, should place the metals in the order of their internal pressures. It is always most striking to consider the series obtained for the substances of highest and lowest internal pressure, for then there is no ambiguity as to the true order, as there is when an element in the middle of the series is chosen for comparison, and when deviations do not differentiate the element of higher internal pressure from the one of lower. Table 5, accordingly, gives the solubilities of Bi and Zn in the series of metals falling between them in Table 2, also those of Sn, in the middle of the series, whose solubilities should show a maximum in the adjacent numbers. The figures were obtained from smooth curves drawn through the points given by the observers cited.

It will be seen that the agreement in the case of Bi is perfect; for Zn it is nearly so, the positions of Cd and Hg being reversed; for Sn the only irregularity is its abnormally great solubility in Bi, corresponding to the result found by Taylor, previously cited. Similar results are obtained with Pb and Cd.

The deviations of amalgams from ideality are best shown by the vapor pressure measurements of the author and his collaborators,[12]

TABLE 5.

SOLUBILITIES OF Bi, Zn AND Sn.

Solvent	Bi at 250°	Zn at 375°	Sn at 180°
Zn	2 liq.[7]	....	0.68[7]
Cd	0.905[10, 11]	0.896[7]	0.71[7, 10]
Hg	0.920[8]	0.904[8]	0.735[9]
Sn	0.933[7]	0.820[7]	....
Pb	0.948[11]	2 liq.[7]	0.735[10]
Bi	....	" "	0.76[7]

[7] Heycock and Neville, *J. Chem. Soc.*, **71**, 383 (1897).

[8] Puschin, *Z. anorg. Chem.*, **36**, 201 (1903).

[9] van Heteren, *Z. anorg. Chem.*, **42**, 129 (1904).

[10] Stoffel, *Z. anorg. Chem.*, **53**, 137 (1907).

[11] Kapp, Dissert. Königsberg (1901).

[12] Zn, Hildebrand, *Trans. Amer. Electrochem. Soc.*, **22**, 319 (1913); Ag, An, Bi, Tl, Hildebrand and Eastman, *J. Am. Chem. Soc.*, **36**, 2020 (1914); **38**, 785 (1916); Cd, Sn, Pb, Hildebrand, Foster and Beebe, *ibid.*, **42**, 545 (1920).

summarized in the plot of $p/p°$ against N shown in Fig. 1. We see here more irregularity than in the other cases. With Cd there is negative deviation, showing that the atoms of these elements attract each other to a greater extent than they attract their own kind. With Zn the deviation is positive, but just as in Table 5, less than we might have expected, which may indicate the same sort of effect as is shown more obviously with Cd, its nearer neighbor in sub-group 2 of the Periodic System. Again Bi, which is below Sn and Pb in Table 2, shows a smaller deviation than Pb and Sn. In brief, Hg seems to

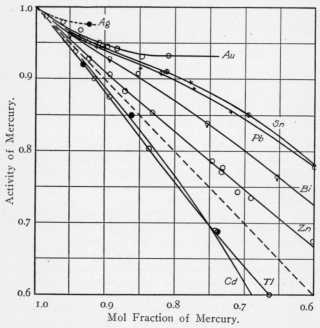

Fig. 1.—Activities of Mercury in Various Amalgams.

show more evidence than we have previously seen of greater attractions for certain other elements than internal pressures alone would lead us to expect. Cases of this sort multiply greatly with other systems to be considered in the following paragraphs. It is interesting to note the great deviations with Ag and Au, which will be found in harmony with the positions of these metals in a later and more extensive table.

The construction of a more general table of internal pressures of metals is made difficult by the lack of accurate data concerning their physical properties in the liquid state, by the inferior accuracy of much of the solubility data and by the frequency with which solid solutions and compounds occur, the former making the freezing point data of less significance for our purpose, and the latter introducing a factor with which the simple internal pressure theory is incompetent to deal. The table we have attempted to construct is therefore somewhat approximate in character and subject to later modification as our knowledge of the field is extended. In its construction we have been guided by what knowledge we possess of the physical properties of the metals, by the freezing point data in cases where simple eutectics occur, by the existence of two liquid phases in many cases, showing extreme mutual insolubility, by the existence of solid solutions of simple type showing great similarity between the components, and by the Periodic System, which we have assumed to indicate the approximate positions of elements that belong to series already established. We have noted in general that internal pressure decreases going from top to bottom of a group. Upon finding, for example, as we have in Table 2, that internal pressures decrease going from Zn to Hg, we feel justified in assuming that the internal pressure of Mg is higher than that of Zn.

The evidence is so large in volume but so inconclusive in many of its individual items that it does not seem worth while to attempt to present it in detail beyond what is shown in Table 6, itself. This table lists the cases in which binary alloys show either two liquid phases or solid solutions, and omits the compounds, which introduce complications rather than contradictions to the internal pressure theory. The data used have been derived from the usual sources, beginning with the Landolt-Börnstein Tabellen.

Each space in Table 6 corresponds to the mixture of the two metals whose symbols are at the left hand side and at the top, respectively. The diagonal is drawn through the intersection of each symbol with itself, so that the nearer a space is to this diagonal the closer are the two metals to each other in internal pressure. The portions of the table on the two sides of the diagonal are, of course, essentially identical, but the presence of both will be found convenient. Those combinations which yield two liquid phases are denoted by i (insoluble), those which yield a complete series of solid solutions by S, and those showing limited solubility in the solid state are denoted by s. Where the system has not been investigated, or where compounds have been found, the space has been left blank so as not to complicate the table.

We must recall, first of all, that the internal pressure theory cannot predict tendencies towards the formation of compounds, or abnormally great attractions between the atoms of unlike metals, so that neither negative deviations from Raoult's law, nor even abnormally small positive deviations, nor, in other words, abnormally great solubilities, are contradictory to the theory. All that can be expected is that insolubility cannot occur unless there is sufficient difference in internal pressure, although even then it may not occur if tendency towards compound formation exists. Let us now examine the table with this in mind. It will be seen that there are no i's within a cer-

TABLE VI

INTERNAL PRESSURE SERIES FOR LIQUID METALS[a]

High ⟵ Internal Pressure ⟶ Low

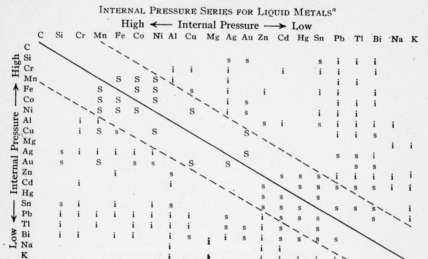

	C	Si	Cr	Mn	Fe	Co	Ni	Al	Cu	Mg	Ag	Au	Zn	Cd	Hg	Sn	Pb	Tl	Bi	Na	K
C																					
Si											s	s				s	i	i	i		
Cr						i	i	i				i				i	i		i		
Mn			S		S	S	i	i								i	i	i			
Fe			S	S		S	s	i	i							i	i		i		
Co			S	S	S			i	s							i	i	i	i		
Ni			S	S	S	S		i	s							i	i	i			
Al			i	i							s	i				s	i	i	i	i	
Cu			i	S	s		S				S					i	i		s		
Mg																			i	i	i
Ag	s		i	i	i	i	i					S				s	s	i			
Au	s		S		s	s	s				S					s	s				
Zn				i		s								s	s	i	i	i	i		i
Cd			i					i					s		s	s	s	s	i		
Hg												s	s	s		s					
Sn	s		i		i		i		s					s	s		s	s	s		i
Pb	i	i	i	i	i	i	i	i		s		i	s	s	s			s			i
Tl	i		i		i		i			s	s		i	s		s					
Bi	i	i		i	i		i			s		i	s	i	s	s	s	s			
Na				i				i	i				i	i		i					
K				i				i					i	i	i	i					

[a] The letters have the following significance: i, 2 liquid phases; S, complete solubility in the solid state; s, limited solubility in the solid state.

tain distance from the heavy diagonal, within the region enclosed by the dotted lines, indicating that there are no cases of insolubility in the liquid state among the metals adjacent to each other. A separation of at least five places is necessary. This may not seem very great, but reference to Table 2 will show that it corresponds to about 100 percent difference in internal pressure, almost as great as the entire difference from top to bottom of the tables in Chapter IX, for non-metallic liquids. There would undoubtedly be found still other insoluble pairs if it were not for differences in boiling point, as between Hg and Fe, which make it difficult or impossible to investigate the system. Even in such cases, however, the table is significant with regard to other phenomena, such as wetting, which likewise requires sufficiently great attractive forces between the two metals concerned. It is well known, for example, that pure Hg will not wet iron.

Turning to the consideration of solubility in the solid phases as an indication of probable likeness in internal pressure of the liquids when compounds are absent, we find that 21 cases of solid solution are found in the spaces between the dotted line and the heavy diagonal, the region in which insolubility in the liquid form is absent, while but 17 cases occur outside this region, although the possible combinations in the two regions are 57 in the former and 153 in the latter. In other words, solid solutions are known to occur in 37 percent of the possible combinations among metals within five places of each other in the internal pressure series, while they are known among but 11 percent of the possible combinations of metals more than four places removed. If we consider metals removed less than eight places from each other, as compared with those eight or more places removed, giving equal numbers of possibilities in the two groups, we find 42 instances of solid solution among the former group and only six among the latter.

Table 6 will be found useful, therefore, in predicting and correlating (a) the solubilities of metals in the liquid, and to some extent, in the solid state; (b) the relative freezing point depressions and apparent molecular weights; (c) the ability of a molten metal to wet another solid metal.

It is expected, also, that it will prove very significant in connection with another phenomenon now under investigation in the author's laboratory, i.e., the initial overvoltage required to start the deposition of one metal upon another.

Whenever it shall prove possible to predict the chemical combinations of metals with each other, this knowledge, together with Table 6, or a perfected form of it, should make it possible to correlate completely all of the intermetallic systems.

Chapter XVII.

Partition of Solutes Between Immiscible Liquids.

When two liquids are practically immiscible in each other it is evident, as explained in Chapter V, that they deviate enormously from Raoult's law. If, then, a solute is introduced which distributes itself between the two solvents, it is evident, further, that its deviations from Raoult's law with respect to the two solvents will be quite different. For example, if the solute obeys Raoult's law with one of

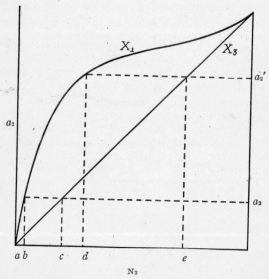

Fig. 1.—Activities of a Solute in Two Different Solvents.

the liquids it will deviate greatly from it with respect to the other liquid.

Let this behavior be represented by Fig. 1 in which the two curves represent the activity of the solute, X_2 in the respective solvents X_1 and X_3. If sufficient of the solute is introduced so that its activity is a_2 when distributed at equilibrium between the two liquids, the ratio of its mol fractions in X_1 and X_3 is ab/ac. If mol fractions are substituted by concentrations, by the aid of the molecular weights and densities, we have the ordinary "partition coefficient," which has been found so useful in getting the activity of one of the components of a complex equilibrium mixture. If, now, we add more X_2 so as to raise its activity in the system to a_2', the ratio of its mol fractions becomes ad/ae, but inspection of Fig. 1 shows that this ratio is by no means the same as at the lower concentration, but that the partition coefficient rises in a way quite predictable from a knowledge of the activity-composition curves. In so far, therefore, as we can determine the latter, we can predict the partition coefficient and its variation with the concentration. The figure also shows that if we restrict ourselves to sufficiently small concentrations so that the activity curves may be regarded as straight, the partition coefficient will remain constant within the same limit.

Since, as explained in Chapter XV, the total activity of an electrolyte does not vary linearly with the concentration, even in dilute solutions, partition coefficients yield the same kind of evidence for ionization as do all other properties which measure activity.

A few examples will serve to illustrate the correlation between partition coefficients and the general principles used throughout this volume. The solubilities of iodine give us a knowledge of its activities in various solvents, which serve to predict the general facts regarding its partition between two solvents. Let us consider its partition between water and carbon bisulfide, bromoform, carbon tetrachloride, respectively, for which we have data by Jakowkin.[1] Like nearly all data upon partition coefficients these refer to amount of solute in unit volume of solution, so that in the absence of densities of the solutions it is impossible to recalculate to mol fractions. However, the conclusions stated above are sufficiently well illustrated by the original figures. Since water corresponds to the solvent X_1 in Fig. 1 and the other liquid to X_3, the partition coefficient, expressed as concentration in X_3 divided by concentration in water, should increase with increasing concentration. That this is the case is shown in Table 1.

TABLE 1.

Conc. of Iodine, g./liter		Ratio Conc. in CS₂ / Conc. in H₂O
in H_2O	in CS_2	
0.0518	30.36	586
0.1104	65.81	596
0.1743	108.3	620
0.2571	167.6	652

A similar increase is shown for the other solvents.

When enough iodine is present to saturate the solution the ratio of the two solubilities should give the partition coefficient, except in so far as the solubilities of the two liquids in each other affects the result. This relation was first pointed out by Berthelot and Jung-

[1] Jakowkin, *Z. physik. Chem.*, **18**, 585 (1895).

fleisch[2] who, however, failed to substantiate it experimentally due
to errors in their figures. Jakowkin, however, later showed it to be
true by the aid of the figures here reproduced in Table 2.

TABLE 2.

PARTITION IN SATURATED IODINE SOLUTIONS.

	Solubility, 25°; g./liter	Ratio found	Ratio calc.
Water	0.3387	...	...
Carbon disulfide	230.0	679	685
Bromoform	189.6	559	559
Carbon tetrachloride	30.33	89.6	89.7

The ratios in the last column were got by extrapolation to saturation of the partition coefficients such as are given in Table 1 for
unsaturated solutions.

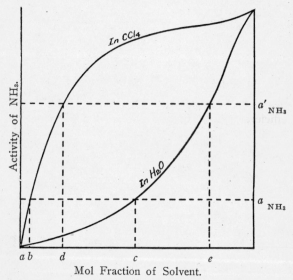

FIG. 2.—Activities of Ammonia in Water and Carbon Tetrachloride.

If we turn to a polar solute, such as ammonia, we find a state
of affairs illustrated in Fig. 2, where the activity of the ammonia in
water is less than that demanded by Raoult's law while in carbon
tetrachloride it is greater, due to the great difference in polarity.
Accordingly, the partition coefficient expressed with the concentration
in the carbon tetrachloride in the numerator, is less than unity and
increases with increasing concentration as shown in Table 3, which
gives partial data by Hertz and Lewy.[3]

[2] Berthelot and Jungfleisch, *Ann. chim. et phys.* 4, 26, 400 (1872).
[3] Hertz and Lewy, *Z. Elektrochem.*, 11, 818 (1905).

TABLE 3.

Molal Concentration of NH_3		
in H_2O	in CCl_4	Ratio
1.73	0.0079	0.00456
2.35	0.0118	0.00502
6.86	0.0464	0.00677
8.59	0.134	0.0156

Since the ionization of the ammonia in the water layer is insufficient to have any marked effect upon the partition ratio, it is usual to attempt to explain the inconstancy of a ratio of this sort by assuming that the solute forms complex molecules in the non-polar liquid. Objections to this practice of ascribing all discrepancies from the ideal solution laws to molecular changes have been given at length in Chapter VII, and apply with equal force here.

Chapter XVIII.

Solubility and Various Related Phenomena.

EFFECT OF SIZE OF PARTICLES UPON SOLUBILITY.

The fugacity of a liquid increases if dispersed into very small drops to an extent given by the equation:[1]

$$RT \ln \frac{f}{f^{\circ}} = \frac{2\gamma v}{r},\qquad (1)$$

where f is the fugacity of the liquid of surface tension γ, molal volume v, dispersed into drops of radius r. The fugacity of the liquid from a plane surface is f°.

We might use this equation to calculate the change in solubility of one liquid in another when a fine emulsion is formed, but it is useful chiefly with respect to the increase in solubility of a solid brought about by fine grinding. In such a case we cannot measure γ except by the equation itself, but we can, nevertheless, draw the qualitative conclusion that since the fugacity of a solid is increased by high dispersion, its solubility must likewise increase in order to maintain equilibrium. The order of magnitude is indicated by the following calculation. In order for the solubility to increase by 10 percent, f/f° must become 1.10. Assuming $\gamma = 100$ dynes, $v = 50$ cc. and $T = 300°$, we have

$$1.03 \times 10^{6} \times 300 \times 2.3 \log 1.1 = \frac{2 \times 100 \times 50}{r},$$

whence $r = 5 \times 10^{-4}$ cm., showing that the particles of such a solid would have to be rather fine in order to show any such increase in solubility. As a matter of fact, Hulett[2] has been able to increase the solubility of gypsum by 20 percent by fine grinding and the solubility of $BaSO_4$ by 80 percent.

This effect is seldom likely to influence determinations of solubility, for in attaining equilibrium sufficient time is usually allowed for the small and more soluble particles to "distill" over on to the larger ones, a process well known to analysts, who let fine precipitates stand in order to become filtrable. The phenomenon may, how-

---

[1] For derivation cf. Lewis and Randall, "Thermodynamics," p. 251, McGraw-Hill Co., 1923. Using vapor pressures instead of fugacities, the equation was first derived by W. Thomson (Kelvin), *Phil. Mag.* [4], **42**, 448 (1871).

[2] Hulett, *Z. physik. Chem.*, **37**, 385 (1901); **47**, 357 (1904).

ever, become important in some cases. For example, if the calomel or mercurous sulfate in normal electrodes or cells is extremely fine the substance will be more soluble, and thus give rise to a different e.m.f. If a finely divided or spongy metal is used as an electrode, it may give an e.m.f. different from that of the less dispersed metal. These differences, of course, tend to disappear on standing, but sufficient time should be allowed for the purpose.

The phenomenon of supersaturation may also be related to Equation 1, for the greater solubility of small particles makes it harder to start crystallization in the absence of crystal "seeds" than it is to continue the crystallization after it is once started. On this account it is often possible to concentrate a solution far beyond its point of saturation for a certain phase, provided this phase is not added to the system, and to maintain indefinitely supersaturated solutions, or even to crystallize from the solution a phase unstable with respect to the first. Thus, by supercooling a solution of Na_2SO_4 it is possible to avoid getting the more stable $Na_2SO_4 . 10H_2O$ and to get the less stable and more soluble $Na_2SO_4 . 7H_2O$.

SURFACE TENSION, ADSORPTION AND SOLUBILITY.

When a substance is dissolved in a liquid with considerable lowering in the surface tension, it is also largely adsorbed or concentrated at the surface. An equation has been derived by Gibbs which connects the surface tension with the adsorption, u_2, which is defined as $\left(\dfrac{\partial N_2}{\partial \sigma}\right)_{\bar{F}_2}$, where σ is surface. It is the number of mols of solute that must be added per unit increase in surface, in order to keep the partial molal free energy of the solute constant. Obviously, where no adsorption at the surface occurs, there is no change in composition of the body of the solution when the extent of its surface is altered, but, when adsorption does occur, increase in surface impoverishes the interior of the liquid in solute, hence solute must be added if the composition of the interior and the partial molal free energy of the solute are to remain unchanged.

The equation of Gibbs [3] is

$$\left(\frac{\partial \gamma}{\partial \bar{F}_2}\right)_{\sigma} = - u_2. \tag{2}$$

Since $\bar{F}_2$ increases with increasing mol-fraction of solute, we see from this equation that if γ is lowered by addition of solute u_2 is positive, and *vice versa*. Wide use has been made of this important qualitative conclusion. It has been customary to assume that $d\bar{F}_2/dN_2$ is given by the laws of the perfect solution, in order to substitute composition for free energy in the above equation, but there is con-

[3] For derivation see Lewis and Randall, "Thermodynamics," p. 249, McGraw-Hill Co., 1923.

siderable objection to this, as the solutions in which adsorption is large, and which therefore interest us most, are those which deviate most from ideal behavior. Let us, therefore, assume a more general equation than Raoult's law, such as Equation V-21, which is

$$\ln f_2 = \ln f_2{}^\circ + \ln N_2 + \tfrac{1}{2}\beta N_1{}^2. \tag{3}$$

This simple equation is, of course, inadequate to express the behavior of all systems, but it will serve our purpose, which is only to bring out the nature of the influence of any deviation from Raoult's law. Writing

$$\left(\frac{\partial \gamma}{\partial N_2}\right)_\sigma = \left(\frac{\partial \gamma}{\partial \overline{F}_2}\right)_\sigma \left(\frac{\partial \overline{F}_2}{\partial N_2}\right)_\sigma, \tag{4}$$

we get the value of the first differential in the right hand member from Equation 2, and the second from Equation 3 as follows:

The relation between $\overline{F}_2$ and f_2 is by definition

$$\frac{\partial \overline{F}_2}{\partial N_2} = RT \frac{\partial \ln f_2}{\partial N_2}, \tag{5}$$

so that, by Equation 3 we have

$$\frac{\partial \overline{F}_2}{\partial N_2} = RT \left(\frac{1}{N_2} - \beta_1 N_1\right). \tag{6}$$

Substituting now in Equation 4 we have

$$\frac{\partial \gamma}{\partial N_2} = - u_2 RT \left(\frac{1}{N_2} - \beta_1 N_1\right). \tag{7}$$

If Raoult's law holds, $\beta_1 = 0$, and the equation reduces to the form usually found, which is also written with concentration, C_2, substituted for N_2,

$$\frac{\partial \gamma}{\partial \ln C_2} = - u_2 RT. \tag{8}$$

When N_2 is small, N_1 is nearly unity and $\frac{1}{N_2} > \beta_1 N_1$ in most cases, so that the same qualitative relation between the signs of $(\partial \gamma/\partial N_2)$ and u_2 is obtained as was stated above. For a given value of $(\partial \gamma/\partial N_2)$, u_2 will be larger the smaller the quantity $(1/N_2 - \beta_1 N_1)$, or the larger is β_1. Since β_1 assumes positive values for positive deviations from Raoult's law, we may summarize finally by stating that *adsorption of a solute at a surface is favored by positive deviations from Raoult's law, as well as by a large decrease in the surface tension upon addition of the solute.* In view of the fact, further, that large differences in internal pressure, as indicated by difference in values of $\gamma/v^{1/3}$ for solvent and solute, accompany positive deviations from Raoult's law, we see that large differences in γ for solvent and solute should usually be accompanied by large values of the adsorption.

These considerations lead to an interesting connection between our theories of solubility and the formation of surface films. When positive deviations from Raoult's law become very large they lead to the formation of two liquid phases. The formation of a second liquid phase upon the surface of a first may also be regarded as a case of very extreme adsorption. The positive deviation and the high degree of adsorption may thus both be regarded as consequences of unlikeness of the two components which causes one to "squeeze out" the other, (cf. Chapter VII) not only into a surface film but also into another phase. If the "solute" consists of a complex molecule, one part of which is "like" the "solvent," another part "unlike," we have the state of affairs investigated especially by Langmuir and by Harkins,[4] where the carboxyl end of a molecule of higher fatty acid is soluble in water, while the hydrocarbon chain is not, so that a stable film is formed upon the surface of the water.

EFFECT OF THE SOLVENT UPON EQUILIBRIUM IN SOLUTION.

If we consider a simple equilibrium, such as

$$(X_1) \rightleftarrows (X_2),$$

the effect of a solvent which tends to unite chemically with, say, X_2, is, of course, to reduce the fugacity of X_2 and to cause X_1 to react to form more X_2. If the concentrations are respectively c_1 and c_2, the equilibrium constant, $K = c_1/c_2$, will be smaller in such a case than in one where no such solvation occurs. Chemists make frequent use of this well known principle, as in the use of H_2SO_4 to displace the equilibrium

$$CH_3COOH + C_2H_5OH \leftrightarrows CH_3COOC_2H_5 + H_2O$$

to the right.

Similarly, if X_2 is more polar than X_1 the use of a polar solvent increases the fugacity of X_1 and decreases that of X_2 so as to make c_1/c_2 small. The equilibrium between triphenyl methyl and hexaphenyl ethane, which may be written simply

$$2\varphi_3 C \rightleftarrows \varphi_3 C C \varphi_3,$$

is displaced towards the polar triphenyl methyl in the more polar solvents, as shown by the well known studies of Gomberg.

The direction of a shift of various tautomeric equilibria with change of solvent can usually be predicted from a consideration of the relative polarity of the two forms.

It is likewise possible to apply the internal pressure theory to determine the direction in which certain equilibria would be displaced, where polarity and compound formation might have little or no effect. Suppose, for example, we are comparing two solvent media of low and high internal pressures, respectively, and that X_1 has a lower internal pressure than X_2. The following scheme will make evident the relative effects upon the concentrations of X_1 and X_2.

[4] Langmuir, *Met. Chem. Eng.*, **15**, 468 (1916); *J. Am. Chem. Soc.*, **39**, 1848 (1917); Harkins, Brown and Davies, *ibid.*, **39**, 354 (1917), and subsequent papers by Harkins and co-workers.

Internal pressure of solvent	low	high
Equilibrium	$(X_1) = (X_2)$	$(X_1) = (X_2)$

Internal pressure of reacting substances	low	high	low	high
Deviation from Raoult's law.....	small	large	large	small
Concentrations at equilibrium....	large	small	small	large

Equilibrium constant, $\dfrac{c_1}{c_2}$........	large	small

In general, we may summarize by saying that *in order to get a large amount of a certain substance in an equilibrium reached in solution one should employ a solvent which is a good one for the substance desired and a poor one for the substance or substances on the other side of the equation of equilibrium. The quality of a solvent in this connection may be determined by any or all of the factors considered in connection with solubility in general, viz., polarity, chemical combination and internal pressure.*

ELECTROMOTIVE FORCE AND SOLUBILITY.

E.m.f. and activity are related through Equation III-17 as follows:

$$\Delta_{F_1} = \mathbf{N}E\mathbf{F} = RT \ln \frac{a}{a_1'}, \qquad (9)$$

where $\mathbf{E}$ denotes the e.m.f. of a cell in which X_1 is transferred from a phase in which its activity is a_1 to one in which it is a_1', $\mathbf{F}$ the Faraday equivalent and $\mathbf{N}$ the number of faradays per mol of substance transferred. The cell may be a metal concentration cell, such as those investigated by Richards and co-workers, and by N. W. Taylor in the author's laboratory. In the former set of investigations the electrodes consisted of amalgams of baser metals at different concentrations with an intermediate electrolyte containing the ion of the base metal. In the latter, an alloy of known composition was measured against a pure electrode of the baser metal, whose activity being unity simplifies Equation 9 to

$$\mathbf{N}E\mathbf{F} = RT \ln a_1. \qquad (10)$$

The Duhem equation makes it possible also to express the e.m.f. in terms of the activity of the other component of the mixture [5]

$$\mathbf{N}E\mathbf{F} = RT \int_{a_2}^{a_2'} \mathbf{N}d \ln a_2. \qquad (11)$$

[5] Cf. Hildebrand, *Trans. Am. Electrochem Soc.*, **22**, 335 (1912); *J. Am. Chem. Soc.*, **35**, 501 (1914).

The measurement of e.m.f. of such cells makes it possible to determine the relation between activity and composition with a high degree of accuracy, far superior to that possible through measurements of vapor pressure or solubility and free from assumptions such as that the vapor obeys the gas laws. Moreover, the system can be investigated over a wide range of temperature, permitting accurate calculation of heat of dilution.

When electrodes of the same metal dip into solutions of its ion at different concentrations connected by a boundary where diffusion occurs, Equation 9 is subject to an uncertain correction for the e.m.f. at the boundary. It is possible, however, to avoid this correction by employing cells without transference and thus make accurate measurements of the activity ratio of an ion at different concentrations.[6] But whether the potential of a liquid junction be avoided in one way or another, it is important to note that the e.m.f. gives activity, and not concentration, unless Raoult's law is obeyed, which is rarely the case with ions in aqueous solution, or unless the solutions are sufficiently dilute to follow Henry's law. In such a case Equation 9 becomes

$$\mathbf{NEF} = RT \ln \frac{N_1}{N_1'}, \tag{12}$$

or using concentrations,

$$\mathbf{NEF} = RT \ln \frac{c_1}{c_1'}. \tag{13}$$

This last equation has been extensively used to determine the solubility of "insoluble" salts, by measuring the e.m.f. of a concentration cell such as

$$Ag \,|\, AgNO_3 \,|\, KNO_3 \,|\, KCl, \; AgCl \,|\, Ag.$$

Knowing the concentration of the $AgNO_3$ and the KCl, it is assumed that the concentration of Ag^+ and Cl^- in these solutions can be calculated. The e.m.f. of the cell is used to give the concentration of Ag^+ in the KCl solution, which is used to calculate the "solubility product" of $AgCl$. Even where the uncertainties due to liquid junctions have been avoided or eliminated, however, the lack of correspondence between activity and concentration, especially in the more concentrated solutions, already discussed in Chapter XV, make the values of solubility so calculated often very inaccurate. Accurate calculations of solubility from e.m.f. measurements are only possible when the relation between activities and concentrations has been determined for the ions involved.

[6] Danner, *J. Am. Chem. Soc.*, **44**, 2832 (1922); Lewis and Randall, "Thermodynamics," pp. 399, 409. McGraw-Hill, 1923.

APPENDIX I.

NOTATION.

a Activity; constant in van der Waals' equation.

b Constant in van der Waals' equation.

c Concentration.

d Complete differential.

e Base of natural logarithms.

f Fugacity.

$f°$ Fugacity of pure liquid.

k Special constants in Equations, VII, 7, 20-23. Eötvös constant.

m Molality.

n Number of mols.

p Vapor pressure.

$p°$ Vapor pressure of pure liquid.

p^s Vapor pressure in the solid state.

q An integer in Equation VII 24; exponent in Equation IX 9-13.

r Mol ratio; radius.

t Temperature (Centigrade); t_b boiling point.

u_2 Mols of solute adsorbed per unit surface.

v Specific volume.

w Weight; mass.

x Number of mols in certain equations in Chapter VII; distance Equations IX 7, 8.

A Atomic weight; constant in Equation IX-2.

B A constant in Equation IX-2.

C A constant in Equation IX-2.

E Internal Energy.

E_σ Surface Energy.

F Free energy.

H Heat content.

K Equilibrium constant.

L Heat of vaporization.

L_f Heat of fusion.

P Pressure.

R Gas constant.

T Temperature (absolute).

T_m Melting point (absolute).

V Volume.

X_1, X_2, etc. Molecular species 1, 2, etc., respectively.

C Molal heat capacities, c_2 of liquid, c of solid.

E Molal internal energy.

F Molal free energy.

$\bar{F}$ Partial molal free energy.

H Molal heat content.

$\bar{H}_m$ Partial molal heat of mixing.

M Molal weight.

N Mol fraction.

V Molal volume.

α Coefficient of thermal expansion; constant in Equations V-3, 7, 17-25; difference between molal volume of an ideal gas and actual molal volume.

β Coefficient of compressibility; constant in Equations V-3, 7, 17-25.

γ Activity coefficient; surface tension.

∂ Partial differential.

μ Ionic strength.

ν Number of ion molecules formed by dissociation of a molecule.

ρ Density.

σ Extent in surface.

φ, ψ A function in general.

Δ Increment.

ln   Natural logarithm.

log   Common logarithm.

C   Centigrade temperature scale.

K   Internal pressure; Kelvin (absolute) temperature scale.

M   Molal, e.g., 0.1 M.

E   Electromotive force.

F   Faraday equivalent.

N   Number of equivalents.

APPENDIX 2.

Papers by the author and co-workers pertaining to solubility referred to in this volume.

The Color of Iodine Solutions (with Ben Leon Glascock), *J. Am. Chem. Soc.*, **31**, 26 (1909).

Uber die Farbe von Jodlösungen, *Z. physik. Chem.*, **74**, 679 (1910).

The Vapor Pressure of Zinc Amalgams, *Trans. Am. Electrochem. Soc.*, **22**, 319 (1912).

The Relation between the Potential of Liquid Amalgam Cells and the Constitution of the Amalgam, *Trans. Am. Electrochem. Soc.*, **22**, 335 (1912).

The Constitution of Certain Liquid Amalgams, *J. Am. Chem. Soc.*, **35**, 501 (1913).

The Vapor Pressure of Silver, Gold and Bismuth Amalgams (with Ermon D. Eastman), *ibid.*, **36**, 2020 (1914).

The Entropy Vaporization as a Means of Distinguishing Normal Liquids, *ibid.*, **37**, 970 (1915).

The Vapor Pressure of Thallium Amalgams (with Ermon D. Eastman), *ibid.*, **37**, 2452 (1915).

Solubility, *ibid.*, **38**, 1452 (1916).

A Study of the System Aniline-Hexane (with Donald B. Keyes), *ibid.*, **39**, 2126 (1917).

The Specific Heats and Heats of Fusion of Triphenylmethane, Anthraquinone and Anthracene (with Alice D. Duschak, A. H. Foster and C. W. Beebe), *ibid.*, **39**, 2293 (1917).

Solubility and Internal Pressure, *ibid.*, **39**, 2297 (1917).

Solubilities of Anthracene, Anthraquinone, Parabromobenzene, Phenanthrene and Iodine, in Various Solvents (with E. T. Ellefson and C. W. Beebe), *ibid.*, **39**, 2301 (1917).

The Vapor Pressure of Liquid Metals, *ibid.*, **40**, 45 (1918).

Solubility. III. Relative Values of Internal Pressures and Their Practical Application, *ibid.*, **41**, 1067 (1919).

The Vapor Pressures of Cadmium, Lead and Tin Amalgams (with A. H. Foster and C. W. Beebe), *ibid.*, **42**, 545 (1920).

Solubility. IV. Solubility Relations of Naphthalene and Iodine in the Various Solvents, Including a Method for Evaluating Solubility Data (with C. A. Jenks), *ibid.*, **42**, 2180 (1920).

Solubility. V. Critical Solution Temperatures of White Phosphorus with Various Liquids (with Theo. F. Buehrer), *ibid.*, **42**, 2213 (1920).

Solubility. VI. Thermodynamic Relation Between Solubility and Internal Pressure, *ibid.*, **43**, 500 (1921).

The Surface Tensions and Densities of Liquid Mercury, Cadmium, Zinc, Lead, Tin and Bismuth (by Thorfin R. Hogness), *ibid.*, **43**, 1621 (1921).

Solubility. VII. Solubility Relations of Rhombic Sulfur (with Clarence A. Jenks), **43**, 2172 (1921).

Theory of Solubility, *Phys. Rev.*, S.S., **21**, 46 (1923).

Solubility. VIII. Solubility Relations of Certain Gases (with Nelson W. Taylor), *J. Am. Chem. Soc.*, **45**, 682 (1923).

Solubility. IX. Metallic Solutions (with T. R. Hogness and N. W. Taylor), *ibid.*, **45**, 2828 (1923).

The Activities of Zinc, Cadmium, Tin, Lead and Bismuth in their Binary Liquid Mixtures, by N. W. Taylor, *ibid.*, **45**, 2865 (1923).

INDEX

Abegg, 98, 105, 109
Acenaphthene, 116
Acetal, 89
Acetaldehyde, 89
Acetamide, 91, 116
Acetanilide, 91, 116, 159
Acetic acid, 86, 116, 127, 159
Acetic anhydride, 116
Acetone,
  as solvent, 131, 159, 173
  internal pressure, 116
  liquid mixtures, 41, 54, 63, 123, 127
  polarity, 89, 91
Acetophenone, 116
Acetonitrile, 89, 91
Acetylene tetrabromide, 89
Acidic and basic character, 118 ff.
Activity, 29
  coefficient, 176
  ionic, 175
  of metals, 182
Addition compounds, 97, 174
Adler, 76, 86, 169, 170, 178
Adsorption, 193
Alcohols, solubilities of salts in, 171 ff.
Alexejeff, 144
Aluminum, 181, 182, 186
  bromide, 116, 157, 174
  chloride, 121, 174
  oxide, 167
Amalgams, 48, 184
Ammonia, 86
  as solvent, 93, 154, 168, 173
  partition, 190
  polarity, 89, 94
  solubility, 135
Amyl acetate, 89, 131
Andrews, 86, 128
Aniline,
  internal pressure, 116
  liquid mixtures, 56, 127, 143, 144
  polarity, 89, 91
  solvent for gases, 131, 136
  solvent for solids, 156, 159
Anisol, 89
Anthracene, 38, 142, 156
Anthraquinone, 38, 116, 156
Antimony,
  tribromide, 116, 174
  trichloride, 116, 121, 174

  pentachloride, 89
Arctowski, 149
Arsenic, 89
  tribromide, 174
Association,
  in pure liquids, 78, 84, 88, 91
  in solutions, 127
Aston, 92
Aten, 151
Atkinson, 138
Atomic volume and polarity, 96
Attraction, intermolecular, see Intermolecular forces
Azoxy anisole, 116

Balloon fabrics, permeability, 138
Baly, 130
Barium,
  carbonate, 167
  fluoride, 170
  sulfate, 166
Basic and acidic character, 118 ff.
Beaver, 86
Beckmann, 128
Beebe, 48, 75, 156, 183
Benedicks, 105
Benzaldehyde, 89, 127
Benzanthrone, 116
Benzene,
  as solvent, 35, 38, 131, 149, 156, 158, 159, 173
  internal pressure, 103 ff., 133
  liquid mixtures, 52, 63, 71, 80, 124, 125, 144
  polarity, 89, 91, 94
Benzil, 116
Benzoic acid, 116, 158
Benzonitrile, 89, 91
Benzophenone, 89, 116
Benzyl alcohol, 89, 91, 127
Benzyl chloride, 144
Berzelius, 86, 118
Billet, 105, 109
Bingham, 93
Bismuth, 52, 93, 181, 182
  bromide, 174
Bissett, 172
Bodländer, 175
Boggs, 179
Boguski, 144